PUBLISHING

Urch Publishing Ltd
PO Box 27554, London, SE4 2PX, United Kingdom
TEL: +44 (0) 20 7639 5464
EMAIL: service@urchpublishing.com

# A Healthy Business

## A guide to the global pharmaceutical industry

### Mark Greener

PUBLISHING

Urch Publishing Ltd
PO Box 27554, London, SE4 2PX, United Kingdom
TEL: +44 (0) 20 7639 5464
EMAIL: service@urchpublishing.com

## About the author

Mark Greener BSc is a former research pharmacologist and well-known writer who specialises in the pharmaceutical industry and clinical medicine. He is currently the Health Editor of the *Pharmaceutical Times* and former editor of *Economic Medicines in Health* and writes regularly for a number of international pharmaceutical publications.

Typeset by Sukie Hunter, 292 Smeeth Road, Marshland St James, Norfolk, TD5 7TD, UK.

Printed in Great Britain by Gomer Press, Carmarthen, Wales.

# Contents

# List of tables

## List of figures

# Foreword

## By Professor Dr Rolf Krebs, DrMed, DrHC
Vice chairman, Boehringer Ingelheim; President, International Federation of
Pharmaceutical Manufacturers' Associations

The pharmaceutical industry is one of the few genuinely high-tech and innovative
areas in the world's economy. It is an engine for improving the quality of life by
curing disease and at the same time it is a powerful economic force in the
countries where it operates.

Rapid progress in biological sciences – in genomics and molecular biology – is
dramatically changing diagnosis and therapy, not only with respect to new
diseases but also in the way today's diseases are treated. The increasing
sophistication of specific diagnostic tests is revealing that diseases currently
described by medical symptoms (such as hypertension) are not at all uniform in
their underlying pathology but can be separated into several distinct individual
conditions that, by mere chance, have similar clinical symptoms. Already this
progress in diagnosis is stimulating research into increasingly specific
compounds and the future will see an explosion of new drugs to meet medical
needs and an unprecedented revolution in therapeutic tools.

Working in this industry is very challenging and stimulating, not just because of
the opportunities it provides in research, development and production of
innovative compounds but also because of the continuous interaction it offers
with the many stakeholders in healthcare – politicians, physicians, pharmacists,
regulators and, most importantly, patients. As so much useful information is now
available on the Internet the industry is moving into an environment where
patients have a basis for true dialogue with their doctors and local regulation is
being outflanked by the huge amount of information on every aspect of drug
treatment available worldwide.

This book will help those who are keen to learn more about the achievements and
success factors driving this industry. It gives an insight into the complexities of
the pharmaceutical industry, the second largest industrial investor in research and
development. This guide shows in detail, and with many real-life examples, the
many aspects that have to be taken into consideration to achieve therapeutic
progress; how marketed products are monitored for safety; and the importance of
adequate information in establishing fully the benefit of medicines.

This book offers a comprehensive overview that can change the way the
pharmaceutical industry is perceived and may create a better basis for dialogue
with the public. I wish it all the success it truly deserves.

# Introduction

As anyone who works in the pharmaceutical industry for more a few weeks soon realises, all too often researchers research, marketers market and never the twain shall meet. Researchers seem to regard marketers as debasing their science in a somewhat sordid struggle for sales. Marketers regard researchers as boffins following esoteric flights of fancy from ivory towers with little or no understanding of the commercially driven real world. And both simply ignore manufacturing, which is, in many ways, the powerhouse of any company. These are caricatures. But like many caricatures, they contain more than an element of truth.

However, this silo mentality is not good for the future of the pharmaceutical industry. Researchers, marketers and manufacturers need to work together to ensure that companies succeed in an increasingly complex, competitive and constantly changing market. And that means understanding and respecting the other disciplines.

To take one example: marketing concerns now influence stop–go decisions in research and development (R&D) to a greater extent than ever before. As a result, it is harder today than 20 years ago for researchers to indulge their curiosity. Ironically, as we will see, this may stifle rather than augment R&D creativity. As John Calam, a world expert on the role of *Helicobacter pylori* in gastrointestinal disease (the recognition of which helped make AstraZeneca's Losec the world best-selling medicine), notes (1996, p. 1): 'We do need medical academics, and part of their role is to play the "mad scientist" and explore the unconventional ideas that larger scientific organisations shun'. To succeed in an increasingly competitive world, the pharmaceutical industry needs both the 'mad' scientists and the pragmatic marketers. While the scientists should be aware of commercial imperatives, marketers need to free researchers' hands to develop the blockbusters of tomorrow. The roots of these blockbusters lie in basic research that, frankly, few marketers are qualified to evaluate. (Well, do you like scientists scrutinising your promotional material?)

On the other hand, the marketing and educational strategy that supports any drug depends on the questions answered during the development programme – a factor that is increasingly important in these days of evidence-based medicine. However, the clinical trials tend to reflect regulatory requirements rather than the needs of the prescribing physician. This can lead to difficulties marketing the agent. With some new treatments for Alzheimer's disease, for example, it is unclear what the improvements in the rating scales, required by the regulatory authorities, meant to patients and their carers. This made it difficult in many parts of the world to persuade physicians, purchasers and providers to prescribe the new agents.

Clinical trials in areas such as Alzheimer's disease need to manage the difficult balancing act of meeting both regulatory and clinical demands. Input from Marketing can help to design studies that are meaningful for the end-user. With the growth in neurological and other CNS conditions, such issues are coming to the fore. Every healthcare professional probably knows what an average 10 mmHg fall in blood pressure means. The clinical value of a 2-point average improvement on a subjective rating scale is harder to quantify.

As a result, I firmly believe that all aspects of the pharmaceutical sector – R&D, manufacturing and marketing – could benefit from a closer dialogue and an appreciation of the issues and demands facing each other's functions. So this book aims first of all to bridge the gaps between research, marketing and manufacturing to give the different parts of the company an insight into how the others work.

However, I also believe that the pharmaceutical industry needs to engage the public in a broader debate. To many of the general public the pharmaceutical industry has a tarnished, if not blackened, reputation. While they rely on medicines when they fall ill, large sectors of the community have real (and, seen from their perspective, justifiable) concerns about the lack of treatments reaching the developing world, the impact of globalisation generally, the use of animals in experiments and the growing use of genomics, to highlight only some topical issues.

The pharmaceutical industry often complains that such arguments are misinformed and represent the views of a vocal minority. And, to a certain extent, this is true. But the pharmaceutical sector hardly goes out of its way to engage in a broader debate. From the outside, drug companies seem secretive and cagey. It is no use arguing that other sectors are just as secretive. Drug companies in particular and health more generally are in the public eye to a greater extent than almost any other sector. It is something senior management needs to recognise and manage.

For example, a recent *Nature* editorial noted that wider public discussion might help to avoid the most vocal interests having a disproportionate influence. On the other hand, scientists, medical professionals and pharmaceutical executives often suggest that the public is not able to properly evaluate scientific data. However, the US National Institutes of Health actively engage the general public in debates about science's ethics and its human impact. They found that the general public has 'little difficulty' understanding the relevant aspects of science to a sufficient degree to take part in consensus conferences on, for example, ethics (*Nature*, 2000). The pharmaceutical industry has little to hide and much to be proud of.

It is worth remembering that the pharmaceutical industry helped to relegate many diseases that our grandfathers and grandmothers most feared to the pages of medical history. Smallpox, polio and many bacterial infections that killed and left people disabled only a generation ago are now treatable and preventable. Vaccination has eradicated smallpox even in countries where the disease was once endemic (Rose, 1993, p. 127).

More recently, pharmaceuticals mean that many cancers are now curable, especially if detected before they spread. AIDS is on the verge of becoming a controllable disease – at least in those countries that can afford modern drugs. And the sector continues to make inroads into the death toll from the so-called 'diseases of civilisation': heart disease, high blood pressure and type 2 diabetes, for instance. In 1971, the death rates in England and Wales from ischaemic heart disease, cerebrovascular disease (stroke) and hypertension (high blood pressure) were 585.4, 323.4 and 37.8 per 100,000 respectively. By 1997, death rates from these diseases had fallen to 451.2, 207.6 and 20.3 respectively. Pharmaceuticals cannot be credited with all of the reduction – improvements in diet and general health are also significant. However, drugs were important.

Nevertheless, there is no room for complacency. The figures also show that there is still some way to go.

Against this background, the book's second aim is to offer a general overview of the international pharmaceutical industry to those inside and outside the sector. Once, people working in a drug company could focus on their market alone. No longer. Drugs may be manufactured on the other side of the world and decisions made in one healthcare system can influence the other. Moreover, many support staff in a modern pharmaceutical company – the personal assistants of senior executives, the human resources departments, and finance – need to appreciate how their sector fits into the broader context.

And I hope the book will provide information to the public, who have a vested interest in the pharmaceutical industry. They have genuine and legitimate concerns about the way pharmceutical companies conduct their business. I hope that this book will offer the general reader an insight into the pharmaceutical sector and help to inform the debate. It is in everyone's interests that these critical debates are conducted from the basis of information rather than ignorance.

Finally, I hope the book will help bring some new blood into the pharmaceutical sector. The pharmaceutical industry is one of the leading powerhouses of the economy in most industrial countries. It is a major employer in many countries and it makes an important contribution to the world's health and wellbeing. Despite this, the drug industry does not appeal to the general public as a career path. Even in the UK, one of the world's leading developers and manufacturers of medicines, only three pharmaceutical companies – Glaxo Wellcome, AstraZeneca and SmithKline Beecham – made the top 50 'ideal employers' in a 1999 survey of graduates.

However, the pharmaceutical industry needs new ideas and insights. The pharmaceutical industry faces pressure from many sides. Increasingly stringent regulatory controls, shorter patent life and growing use of generics, as countries worldwide try to contain costs, conspire to undermine companies' profitability and their ability to undertake research and development. R&D costs continue to rise and there are fewer new product launches from the large companies at least to sustain the growth seen over the last few years (Grabowski, 1982).

These factors mean that the sector's growth may be below the double figures traditionally expected by stockbrokers and shareholders. In response, leading pharmaceutical companies responded by merging into ever-larger conglomerates and forging numerous alliances with academia and smaller companies. (If you are an academic considering an alliance with a drug company, you should at least understand how your partner operates.) But while the mania for mega-mergers seems to be a new trend, it has in fact been a feature of the sector since it began in the back rooms of pharmacies and in dye manufacturers' laboratories. Indeed, most of the major companies drove their growth through a policy of acquisition and merger. However, as we will see there is a real question about whether the current spate of mergers will foster long-term sustainability in the sector.

On the other hand, the first years of the new millennium should also offer numerous opportunities for novel, innovative therapies. Claims for the potential offered by the Human Genome Project are often overstated, at least in the short term. However, genomic research has the potential to produce millions of new targets. Despite all the advances, researchers have only scratched the surface of human biology. Genomics will allow researchers to dig much deeper. Add to this new high-tech R&D tools and the pharmaceutical sector's success should continue.

For instance, it is a truism that we live in an information age. We face a proliferation of choice of magazines, books and multimedia. As anyone in R&D or medicine knows, it is now impossible to remain up to date in any field, let alone in science more generally. Yet, as one commentator noted recently (Mulgan, 1996), the growth in information leads to a paradox. One the one hand, the world is now less comprehensible than it was for our ancestors. (I would phrase this somewhat differently: perhaps we are just more aware of how incomprehensible the world actually is.) On the other, there is 'an exponential growth of theoretical possibilities.... The explosion of scientific knowledge means that there are many more areas where unpredictable advances are now possible, or likely.' The link between *H. pylori* and ulcers is the best example of this. Few researchers expected to find the cure for gastric ulcers in a microbiology lab. The Human Genome Project and advances in other areas of biomedical science should offer unprecedented advances for human health and wellbeing. Current drugs target only some 400 sites in the body. Genomics will increase the possible sites of interventions into the thousands (*Pharmaceutical Journal*, 1999).

But there is no room for complacency. To maximise the return on investment, everyone in the sector must understand and appreciate the issues facing other parts of the industry. It is more critical than ever that society debates the ethical and political issues surrounding the sector from the basis of information, not ignorance. And, if the world is to maintain the successful treatment of the diseases of the new millennium, the sector needs new ideas.

I hope that this book introduces some of these key issues. As with any review of this kind, I am a dwarf standing on the shoulders of giants. So I have also included a comprehensive bibliography, which should help those of you interested to look at a particular issue in more detail. I have also included a number of examples to illustrate the points made in the book. These are just that – examples – and are not intended to be comprehensive.

4

# Chapter 1: A brief history of the pharmaceutical industry

It is sobering to reflect that while diseases killed and disabled even before our ancestors became human, the pharmaceutical industry – at least in a recognisable, modern form – has existed for less than 150 years. Yet over this time, the pharmaceutical industry grew from humble mid-19th-century origins, often in pharmacists' backrooms or the laboratories of dye manufacturers, into a global industry encompassing some 10,000 companies. However, just 100 companies form the backbone of the global industry, making the approximately 5,000 medicines that physicians use in routine practice (Walsh, 1998, p. 3). Many of the other companies either make niche products or develop new drugs, which they license to the larger players. There is also a large outsourcing industry supporting these companies (Chapter 5).

However, we have always needed medicines. Some of the herbs and minerals used by our ancestors, in alternative and complementary medicine and in the less developed parts of the world seem to be pharmacologically active. While no one should trivialise the technological advances made by medical science generally and the pharmaceutical industry in particular, up to 40% of the plants in some old herbals were probably effective. Today, some of the best-known drugs – aspirin, penicillin and cyclosporin to name three – derive from natural products. Indeed, 39% of the 520 new drugs approved between 1983 and 1994 were either natural products or derived from nature. Among antibacterial and anticancer drugs, the proportion was even higher – between 60% and 80% (Greener, 2000a). Against this background, many issues facing today's pharmaceutical industry resonate across the centuries: regulation to ensure a medicine's quality; concerns about the cost of therapies; avoiding toxicity, for instance.

For all the modern industry's technological sophistication, for all the high-tech 'big science' of the Human Genome Project, for all its industrial muscle (see Chapter 2), today's pharmaceutical industry represents the culmination of several historical trends. So we will begin our survey of the global sector by looking briefly at the history of the pharmaceutical industry.

## Traditional treatments

The story begins with medical plants and minerals used by traditional healers. As we will see, some are still used today in mainstream medicine as well as by herbalists. However, the knowledge that plants, minerals and animal products can heal is probably as old as the human race (Jackson, 1988, p. 75). And some traditional treatments were undoubtedly effective.

Almost 5,000 years ago – in 2735 BC – the Chinese emperor Shen Nung wrote a herbal. He described one preparation for fever – *Ch'ang Shang* – that contains plants we now to be effective against malaria. Similarly, we now realise that many preparation from plants are undoubtedly effective: digitalis from the foxglove, used to treat heart disease; quinine from the bark and roots of *Cinchona* plants, for malaria; and ipecacuanha from *Cephaelis* plants, for dysentery, to name three (Walsh, 1998, p. 3). And, of course, the opium poppy's ability to counter pain has been employed therapeutically since Roman and Greek times. Egyptian physicians used senna pods to treat constipation and peppermint to alleviate indigestion. The former is still used by doctors today, while peppermint is an ingredient in many popular over-the-counter medicines for heartburn.

Indeed, classical physicians could chose from a remarkably wide number of therapies for diseases. The Greek *De materia medica*, written in 64 AD, included around 600 herbal remedies, for example. And while modern life is often seen as 'the age of anxiety', analysis of written texts shows that anxiety was recognised in classical Rome and Greece. The ancients also recognised social alienation (Newbold, 1990) – which today we might characterise as social phobia, a rapidly growing market.

Of these early healers, the Graeco-Roman physician Galen, who lived around AD 130–200, casts the longest shadow, stretching as far as Jacobean medicine. Galen's idea that illnesses arose from imbalances in four 'humours' was the predominant medical idea for almost 1,500 years (Jackson, 1988, p. 76). So Roman and medieval medicine aimed to balance the four humours: blood, phlegm, yellow bile and black bile. Each corresponded to one of the Aristotelian elements – air, water, fire and earth respectively – and conveyed characteristic properties of heat and moisture. Ideally, treatment aimed to render patients slightly warm and moist. However, how far this could be achieved depended on age, sex and area. The elderly were said to be colder and drier than younger people, while menstruating women were colder and wetter than men (Laudan, 2000). To restore the balance, Galen suggested using a variety of herbs, minerals and animal products. Many were probably effective. Estimates vary, but perhaps 20–40% had some therapeutic benefit. Many of the other patients would have benefited from the placebo effect (Jackson, 1988, p. 80).

But some of Galen's ideas lasted even longer. For instance, Galen was among the first to insist on the purity of drugs. So, for instance, he insisted on using the right species and age of plants and often obtained the plants himself (Jackson, 1988, p. 80). Today, ensuring the quality and purity of medications and the source of raw ingredients remains one of the regulatory authorities' most important roles and is a major concern for the industry.

Similarly, the commercialisation of medication extends back millennia. A trade in *materia medica* flourished in Greek and Roman cities. The choice was staggering: Pliny notes some 900 substances in his *Natural History*, some imported from the far-flung reaches of the Roman Empire. However, Pliny, along with a number of other Graeco-Roman writers, criticised the public's gullibility and questioned the cost and benefit of the some more exotic remedies – predating the pharmaco-economic debates raging today. Indeed, the emperor Diocletian (AD 245–313) issued the *Edictum de maximis pretiis*, which set maximum prices for products including herbal medicines, such as cinnamon bark, ginger and saffron (Potzsch, 1998, p. 27). Without pushing historical analogies too far, this is almost an antecedent for pricing and reimbursement today. At least it illustrates the same concern – ensuring that medicine is affordable.

## The Dark Ages

The Hippocratic writings dominated medieval medicine – doctors still swear the Hippocratic oath in many countries today. They were collected around 400 BC and then systematised by Galen some 600 years later. These ideas persisted among Islamic intellectuals after the Roman Empire declined and fell. However, by the 12th century, European scholars had translated most of the main Arabic texts into Latin. Such textbooks were used in the medical schools, such as Montpellier in Southern France. From the 15th century, Greek manuscripts augmented the Latin texts (Laudan, 2000).

During the Middle Ages, healers' choices were limited largely to the herbs that they could grow in gardens (often in monasteries) or gather from local woods and hedgerows; minerals they could find in the ground; and animals they could catch. However, the choice increased markedly in later medieval times, driven by the foundation and rapid expansion of global trade. By the 15th century Venetian galleys often shipped at least 40 different pharmaceuticals into London from, among other places, the East Indies, Ceylon, India, Persia and Egypt. The cost and scarcity of these no doubt contributed to their perceived value (Rawcliffe, 1995, p. 151). But again, some commentators questioned whether the benefit of some of these herbs and spices really warranted the high prices often charged.

Around this time, the natural philosophers (the forerunners of today's scientists) also began to develop some of the therapeutic principles that still underpin drug development. For example, Theophrastus Philippus Aureolus Bombastus von Hohenheim (1493–1541) – better known as Paracelsus – was, for a time, professor of medicine and town physician of Basel, in Switzerland (Adams, 2000, p. 31), the centre for Swiss pharmaceutical companies. Paracelsus made numerous pharmacological advances and encouraged a move toward chemical treatments and away from herbal treatments (Adams, 2000, p. 31). Moreover, Paracelsus was among the first natural philosophers to recognise the relationship between dose and the risk of developing side-effects. (Indeed, the Greek *pharamakon* – the root of the words pharmacy, pharmacology and pharmaceutical – means both medicine and poison.)

For example, in 1530 Paracelsus argued that carefully measured doses of mercury compounds taken internally could counter syphilis. His idea was not, at first, enthusiastically welcomed – which, given mercury's toxicity, is not perhaps surprising. However, by Elizabethan times, barber–surgeons commonly used drugs based on mercury to treat syphilis. While mercurial compounds can be effective, they also cause a number of side-effects and even death, through kidney damage, and the dose needed to be carefully controlled (Adams, 2000, p. 59). Nevertheless, Paracelsus's insight formed the basis of the dose–response relationship still assessed today.

In general, however, physicians relied on plant-based treatment, which they tended to formulate themselves. Shakespeare's son-in-law John Hall, become 'one of the most dedicated and sought-after physicians' around Stratford-upon-Avon and dispensed 'innovative herbal remedies' for numerous major and minor ailments (Holden, 1999, p. 316).

While Hall and many of his contemporaries did their best to alleviate their patients' suffering, there was little supervision of the quality of the concoctions the physicians prescribed. Moreover, fraud was rife and pressure began to grow for greater regulation. To many people, apothecaries and their clinician allies hoodwinked the public into buying 'over-priced, adulterated and largely useless decoctions'. As a result, local civic authorities and the medical profession introduced rafts of regulations, albeit with limited success. As long ago as 1268, apothecaries in Venice were bound by codes of practice to ensure that their medications were of a certain quality. Failure meant fines and even corporal punishment (Rawcliffe, 1995, pp. 148–154).

Partly in response to the growing tide of public opinion swelling against them, and to protect their business, the Society of Apothecaries was founded in London in 1618. Before then, apothecaries were members of the Grocers' Company. Members of the Society of Apothecaries began to take on the role of general practitioners (Adams, 2000, p. 79), offering advice to patients who could not afford to consult a doctor. In the 18th century, some become general practitioners, and chemists (who, as their name suggests, dealt in chemicals) merged with druggists (who dealt in animal and vegetable products). In 1815, an act of Parliament legally established their right to buy, compound, dispense and sell drugs (Jackson, 1996, p. 3).

The same year as the Society of Apothecaries was founded, the *London Pharmacopoeia* was published. This was mandatory across England. While the *London Pharmacopoeia* was the first national pharmacopoeia, a German pharmacopoeia had been published in 1546, followed by one in Basel in 1561 and in Augsburg 3 years later. These pharmacopoeias form the basis of formal regulation of drug composition and quality and are still used today.

## The role of pharmacists in the origins of the drug industry

Apothecaries were the ancestors of modern professional pharmacists. And across Europe and America, pharmacists sowed the seeds that grew into many of today's major drug companies. For example, Allen & Hanburys, which grew into Glaxo Wellcome, began in Old Plough Court in the City of London in 1715. However, it would be many years before the chemist shop developed into a pharmaceutical company.

In the meantime, pharmacists survived by formulating their own medicines. One pharmacy toward the end of the 18th century had a turnover of £720 a year. Drugs and medicines accounted for £420. Patent medicines (which were not made by the pharmacist) accounted for only £66 (*Plough*, 1933). Nevertheless, even 200 years ago, medicines made by outside companies accounted for just under 10% of a pharmacist's turnover.

During the 19th century, pharmaceutical sciences began developing intellectual respectability – marked by the launch of influential journals, such as the *Journal de pharmacie et de chimie*, first published in 1809, and the international pharmaceutical congress, first held in 1865. Over the course of the century, pharmacists began purifying, standardising numerous natural remedies and isolating the active ingredients (see box).

These isolates gave the first pharmacologists drugs (although they were impure and nonselective compared to today's pharmacological probes) to dissect how the body works. Nicotine, for example, stimulates receptors on neuromuscular junctions and ganglia, which is reflected in their name: nicotinic receptors.

| Landmarks in the isolation of pharmacologically active ingredients in plants |
| :---: |
| Morphine from the opium poppy (1806) |
| Narcotine from the opium poppy (1803) |
| Emetine from ipecac root (around 1817) |
| Strychnine from nux vomica, the seeds of the *Strychnos* tree (about 1817) |
| Quinine from cinchona bark (1820) |
| Nicotine from the tobacco plant (1828). |
| Cocaine from coca leaves (1860) |
| Atropine from *Atropa belladonna* – the deadly nightshade (1883) |

Atropine – usually isolated from *Atropa belladonna* but also found in plants such as jimsonweed, stinkweed and thorn apple – blocks the action of acetylcholine and started the characterisation of the muscarinic receptor family. The roots of modern scientific and molecular pharmacology lie in these pioneering studies: they gave the chemists a target to aim at.

However, progress was slow. For example, the German pharmacist Friedrich Serturner purified morphine in about 1803. However, it was not until 1923 that chemists unravelled its chemical structure and the early 1950s before it could be synthesised (Sneader, 1998).

Nevertheless, a derivative of morphine was one of the fledgling pharmaceutical sector's first commercial successes. Two English chemists, G. H. Beckett and Charles Alder Wright, synthesised heroin (diacetylmorphine) in 1874. But their research was not picked up in the UK (Miller and Tran, 2000). In 1898, Joseph von Mering, who was to develop hypnotic barbiturates, synthesised heroin among 18 morphine derivatives for the German company E. Merck of Darmstadt. Heroin was weaker than morphine against cough and pain. So E. Merck marketed ethylmorphine as a cough suppressant (Sneader, 1998). However, a researcher at Bayer – Heinrich Dreser – recognised the potential of diacetylmorphine. The research produced the most extensive scientific literature that had emerged from an industrial pharmacology laboratory up to that time. Originally, Bayer scientists believed that heroin would suppress cough and aid breathing in people with severe lung disease, such as tuberculosis (Sneader, 1998). The details of how heroin was named may never be known. There appear to be several apocryphal stories. According to one, heroin was named after the German word *heroisch* ('strong'), with reference to its effects (Miller and Tran, 2000). According to another story, heroin was named after *Heros,* a German term for an ancient Greek hero (Sneader, 1998). These suggestions share, however, a recognition that heroin was more powerful than morphine (Miller and Tran, 2000).

Heroin also became one of the first products of the pharmaceutical industry to be tightly regulated. It was available over the counter in the early part of the 20th century. However, the increasing number of addicts began to concern politicians, physicians and the general public. So in December 1914, the US congress passed the Harrison Act, which introduced federal controls and set a maximum permitted amount of heroin that could be included in proprietary preparations (Sneader, 1998).

As this example shows, the commercialisation of pharmacological advances rapidly gained pace. Indeed, the growing number of commercial medicines prompted the *Journal de pharmacie et de chimie* to publish monthly information sheets on new medicines, side-effects and withdrawals from the market (Rey, 1993, p. 238). As a result of the increasing competition among medicines, marketing became more aggressive. However, the growing number of patent remedies that were nationally advertised, often backed with adverts, made unsustainable claims (Jackson, 1996, p. 17).

Nevertheless, the formulation of medicines was beginning to move away from pharmacists' back rooms and into the commercial sector. A growing number of small companies began producing medicines. In 1859, for example, the French company Etienne Poulenc began producing minerals and chemicals for photographic and therapeutic uses from its factory in Ivry. Usines du Rhône was founded in 1885, followed by Roussel some 15 years later (Rey, 1993, p. 130). These companies went on to form part of Rhône-Poulenc-Rorer (now Aventis) and Hoechst-Marion-Roussel, two of France's leading pharmaceutical companies.

Meanwhile, in Germany several companies arose to meet the growing demands for pure, standardised extracts of widely used herbal remedies, which were in short supply because of the limited numbers of apothecaries. In the 14th century, several medicinal chemicals – such as sal ammoniac, mercury chloride and borax – were manufactured in 'quasi-industrial' quantities (Potzsch, 1998, p. 243). However, the new companies embraced the industrial revolution and produced industrial quantities of a product.

There was growing recognition among the medical profession and general public that pure natural remedies meant that physicians could administer accurate doses as well as reducing the risk of side-effects due to impurities. Several well-known companies began to meet this demand – include one founded by Heinrich Immanuel Merck at the Golden Apothecary in Darmstadt. Schering AG arose from the Green Apothecary in Berlin, while Carl Engelhardt in Frankfurt founded the company that gave rise to Boehringer Ingelheim and its namesake in Mannheim (Drews, 1999, p. 25).

## The second strand

The apothecary tradition was one of two strands in the mix of elements that led to the modern pharmaceutical industry. The second developed from the aniline dye industry. Much of the 19th century industrial machine was fuelled by the carbonisation of hard coal. This produced coal gas, which powered most of the industrialised nations' civic lighting, and coke, which fuelled the industrial furnaces. However, carbonisation of hard coal left coal tar, a complex mix of chemicals. Coal tar is still used today to treat some skin diseases (Drews, 1999, p. 23). More importantly, the research into coal tar led to modern, synthetic chemotherapeutics (using chemicals rather than natural products to treat disease).

However, chemists soon recognised that coal tar proved a rich source of dyes that, with relatively simple chemical modification, could make almost any colour in the spectrum. The first aniline dye was made in 1856 by the English chemist Sir William Henry Perkin, ironically as part of attempts to synthesise the antimalarial quinine. Companies such as Bayer, Hoechst, Ciba and Geigy began manufacturing a variety of products, including dyes and pharmaceuticals, from coal tar (Drews, 1999, p. 23).

## The antibiotic triumph

Some three decades after Perkin's discovery, the German chemist Paul Ehrlich found that methylene blue, a synthetic dye, was antimalarial. His experiments between 1901 and 1904 led Ehrlich to develop the 'side-chain' theory, which correlated chemical structure with biological effects. This forms the basis of the structure–function analysis widely used in modern drug development. Ehrlich also discovered, around 1909–10, the organic arsenic-derived drug arsphenamine. Marketed as Salvarsan, arsphenamine was the first really clinically effective syphilis treatment that did not have serious, dose-limiting side-effects. Over the next few years, numerous other chemotherapeutics followed, including mepacrine, proguanil, chloroquine and, most importantly, the sulphonamides.

Several years before, in the late 19th century, researchers had recognised that certain synthetic azo dyes eradicated some bacteria in the test tube. However, these were ineffective in animals. But several decades later, German researchers found that chemicals derived from the red dye prontosil rubrum were effective in vivo and in vitro. In the early 1930s, the German company I. G. Farbenindustrie patented Prontosil and other azo dyes containing a sulphonamide group. The company was the first to use sulphonamides therapeutically, curing a 10-month-old child of staphylococcal septicaemia. The discoverers won the 1938 Nobel Prize in Medicine. Eventually, I. G. Farbenindustrie and other companies tested more than 6,000 sulphonamides. Today, pharmacologists are revisiting drugs, such as the phenothiazines (see below), that are closely related to methylene blue in the hope that they might overcome resistance and enhance the effectiveness of modern antibiotics (Tan et al., 2000).

Nevertheless, the discovery of penicillin by Sir Alexander Fleming in 1928 and its development by Sir Howard Florey and Ernst Chain overshadowed the Germans' achievement. The story is too well known to recite here. Drug companies began mass-producing penicillin in 1943 and the antibiotic was widely used during the Second World War. Sadly, resistance was first reported in 1947 (Tan et al., 2000). Fortunately, penicillin was followed by other important antibiotics such as erythromycin, the tetracyclines, the macrolides and the cephalosporins, the first of which was isolated in 1961. Nevertheless, the 'constant overuse' of antibiotics in animals and humans means that some bacterial strains are now resistant to almost every antibiotic (Tan et al., 2000).

It is important to remember that, before the sulphonamides and penicillin, infectious diseases imposed a huge toll on society. Looking back with the benefit of today's antibiotics, it is easily to forget just how devastating infectious diseases were. For example, pulmonary or respiratory tuberculosis, also called consumption, was consistently the single largest cause of death in late 19th century London. There were also small, short-lived smallpox epidemics (Mooney et al., 1999). As Table 1.1 shows, standardised death rates from infections declined dramatically between the mid-19th century and the early 1970s. The change between the mid-19th century and 1901 represents, largely, the impact of public health initiatives (such as the provision of sanitation and clean water).

### Table 1.1: Standardised death rates per thousand of the population

| Disease | 1848–54 | 1901 | 1971 |
|---|---|---|---|
| Airborne infections (e.g. TB, pneumonia) | 7.27 | 5.12 | 0.62 |
| Water and food borne infections (e.g. cholera, dysentery) | 3.66 | 1.93 | 0.04 |
| All infections | 12.97 | 8.47 | 0.71 |

Source: based on Cherry, 1996, p. 15

Antibiotics are largely responsible for the change up to 1971 (although the table also shows that we still have some way to go to eradicate these common killers).

Aniline dyes also gave rise to the first non-natural psychoactive drugs – the phenothiazines. These were synthesised during the late 19th century as part of an attempt to develop dyes such as methylene blue. In the late 1930s, a derivative, promethazine, was found to be sedative. Promethazine is still used today, but the search for other phenothiazine derivatives led, in 1949–50, to chlorpromazine, the first effective treatment for schizophrenia. Haloperidol followed a few years later. Today, with the advent of more effective and better tolerated drugs (the 'atypical antipsychotics'), scientists and medics tend to highlight the limitations of these older neuroleptics. At the time, however, they were considered almost wonder drugs, clearing the psychiatric wards of people with florid psychotic symptoms such as hallucinations. Sometimes, with the often justified enthusiasm that greets a new drug, as well as with the activities of sales and public relations companies to highlight the limitations of conventional treatments, it is easy to forget how important the older drugs are.

## The young drug industry goes west into early merger mania

While globalisation is often considered a modern phenomenon, the fledgling pharmaceutical companies rapidly expanded worldwide. Hoffmann-La Roche entered the US market in 1905, followed by Sandoz a few years later. E. Merck came to New York, some 60 years after being founded in Darmstadt, in 1827. Schering began selling diphtheria antitoxin in the years before the First World War. However, Merck and Schering, being German owned, were seized under the Alien Property Custodian Act during the war. Both became independent private American companies (Drews, 1999, p. 27) – eventually forming Merck Sharp & Dohme and Schering-Plough – but leading to confusion ever since! There was even, in the early years of this century, a global brand – Aspirin (see box).

### The American way

The growth of pharmaceutical companies was not confined to Europe. Several of today's large players companies arose in the US, including: Smith, Kline & French; Wyeth; E. R. Squibb & Sons; Parke, Davis & Co.; Eli Lilly (founded by a chemist); G. D. Searle; Lederle; Upjohn; and Abbott, among others. These often began with pharmacists formulating patent medicines – sold by the medicine men

## The first global brand

Despite what advertising and marketing gurus might tell you, global brands are nothing new. Aspirin, introduced in 1897, was the first global brand. The world's favourite medicine has its roots in observations made by a mid-18th century English cleric, the Reverend Edmund Stone, that willow bark alleviated fever. In 1829, the French chemist Pierre Leroux isolated the bitter glycoside salicin from willow bark and showed that it reduced fever. Chemical manipulations led to sodium salicylate, which was used to treat rheumatic fever, fever generally and gout from 1875. A French chemist – Charles Frederic Gerhard – isolated acetylsalicylic acid, another chemical modification, in 1853.

Gerhard's work was neglected until Felix Hoffman, a Bayer chemist, demonstrated acetylsalicylic acid's anti-inflammatory effects in his father, who was crippled by arthritis. The company was receptive to the idea that side-chain substitution could reduce the risk of side-effects. Bayer marketed an antidiarrhoeal preparation, Tannigen, in 1894. Tannigen was prepared by acetylating phenolic hydroxyl groups. Bayer believed that the acetylating the side chain lessened irritation in the mouth and stomach. Tannigen was widely used until the 1950s (Sneader, 1998). Despite this, Hoffman's superior – Heinrich Dreser, the inventor of heroin – rejected the drug. (It wasn't to be the last major drug whose value was questioned by the boss!) Acetylsalicylic acid languished on the shelves for a year until Carl Duisberg, the researchers' ultimate boss, saw its potential (Mann and Plummer, 1991, pp. 15–31).

Acetylsalicylic acid was launched as Aspirin – the name is derived from the scientific name of the meadowsweet (Spiraea), the plant species from which salicylic acid was isolated – in 1899. Aspirin rapidly became the first global pharmaceutical brand – as well as spawning numerous imitators and me-toos (drugs developed to cash in on a market with little if any additional clinical benefit).

For example, in 1906, Bayer introduced aspirin into the US and, after a few years, opened a factory to supply the local market. Aspirin was also the first drug to rely on brand-led advertising to distinguish the Bayer version from the other analgesics, especially after the patent expired just before the First World War. During the 1920s and 1930s, Bayer used paper and radio advertising and attractively decorated trucks on the streets of Europe. Moreover, aspirin manufacturers developed markets in Asia, Africa and Latin America, who had previously relied on traditional healers. The cheap currency allowed the companies to promote brands heavily using posters, radio adverts and sound trucks. Aspirin spread worldwide to become Aspro in Australia and Melhoral in South America. Aspirin remains today, more than 100 years after its launch, a mainstay of medicine cabinets worldwide and helps to reduce the risk of heart attacks. (See Mann and Plummer, 1991 for further details.)

in the wild West – and in some cases grew by merger. Indeed, merger mania characterised the drug industry from its earliest days. The stories of Johnson & Johnson and Bristol-Myers Squibb, other leading American companies (page 115 and box below), also show how leading companies grew by mergers and acquisitions.

For instance, the German and French pharmacists Seitler and Zeitler opened a drug business in Philadelphia. Their accountant and interpreter, George Smith, and his bookkeeper, Mahlon Kline, later bought Seitler and Zeitler out. They then merged with a perfume manufacturer, Harry French, to form Smith, Kline & French. The company merged some years ago with Beecham of the UK. Today,

SmithKline Beecham markets over 400 branded products. And, of course, SmithKline Beecham is set to merge with Glaxo Wellcome to form the world's largest drug company.

Its new partner, Glaxo Wellcome, also grew by merger and acquisition. In the 1930s, Allen & Hanburys were still adverting 'delicious, nourishing and sustaining' glucose toffees, beef juice and Lixen – elixir of senna pods, a laxative (*Plough*, 1933). However, Allen & Hanburys had already begun to move from plant-based medicines into synthetic chemicals and, by the end of the Second World War, helped move science into the driving seat behind pharmaceutical innovation. Then, in May 1958, Allen & Hanburys joined with Glaxo. The *Daily Mail*, a British newspaper, described the union as 'a take-over bid of the best kind'. The merger allowed the company to fund a period of rapid growth and help Glaxo develop, among many others, ranitidine (Zantac). Developed in the 1970s, ranitidine was the second $H_2$-receptor antagonist launched for gastrointestinal ulcers. However, through clever marketing, ranitidine outsold cimetidine to become the first billion-dollar 'blockbuster'. During the 1980s and 1990s, Glaxo continued to grow, partly by merger and acquisition, most notably with Wellcome.

The pharmaceutical companies' early growth relied on their reputation for quality. As mentioned above, the content and quality of many products varied between manufacturer and between batches. Smith, Kline & French wanted to market across the country and so had large-scale production and manufacturing. As a result, it won the contract to supply the US army with quinine during the war with Mexico. E. R. Squibb and Wyeth had obtained the contracts during the Civil War (Healy, 1997, pp. 17–18).

---

### The making of Bristol-Myers Squibb

In 1887, William McLaren Bristol and John Ripley Myers invested $5,000 in a near-bankrupt ethical pharmaceuticals business, although neither had any experience in the area. It proved a lucrative investment. Today, Bristol-Myers Squibb is worth $12bn, with more than 47,000 employees in more than 130 countries. However, the biggest impetus to its growth came with the merger with the Squibb Corporation in 1989, at the time the largest merger in the history of the healthcare industry. The Quaker Edward Robinson Squibb had founded Squibb in 1858.

---

## The biotech revolution

The biotech revolution also had humble beginnings, with Gregor Mendel's experiments on the garden pea in the mid-19th century. Around 100 years later, in 1953, James Watson and Francis Crick described DNA's double helix, with the so-called central dogma (the flow of information from the gene to RNA to protein) postulated in 1958 (Kanehisa, 2000, pp. 1–23). This is discussed in more detail in Chapter 4.

Since then, progress has been rapid. Academic researchers began developing genetic engineering during the late 1960s and early 1970s. In 1973, researchers announced the first successful use of recombinant DNA technology – the cornerstone of genetic engineering (Harvard, 1991). Methods for DNA sequencing, today used to map the genome, followed 2 years later. In 1977, researchers sequenced their first organism, a virus ($\phi\chi$174) of 5,000 nucleotides and 11 genes. The 1.5m nucleotides and 1,700 genes of the first free-living organism, *Haemophilus influenzae*, were sequenced in 1995. In contrast, the human genome contains some 3bn nucleotides and perhaps 100,000 genes (Kanehisa, 2000, pp. 1–23).

By 1976, technology had advanced sufficiently to prompt Eli Lilly to invite researchers at Harvard, the newly formed biotechnology company Genetech and the University of California at San Francisco to take part in a symposium to develop synthetic human insulin. By the end of 1977, the Genetech team reported that they had for the first limed expressed a human protein gene, for human somatostatin, in bacteria. Meanwhile, Novo Industri in Europe was also trying to develop recombinant human insulin. Lilly reached the US market first in 1983, while Novo Industri had launched in Europe the year before (Harvard, 1991).

Since then, the biotech revolution has continued apace. Protein and polypeptide drugs represent an increasingly important part of the worldwide pharmaceutical market. Indeed, 38 of the top 100 drugs are peptides. In 1997, the worldwide sales for peptide and protein drugs reached $13bn, but analysts expect the market to grow to $24bn by 2002. The current stage of play in the sector is discussed in Chapter 9.

This expansion will be fuelled in part by the sequencing of the human genome (see Chapter 4), which began in the late 1980s. Molecular biology's greater understanding of functional genomics (how a gene's products act), post-transcriptional modification (the body's processing of the gene product) and the second messenger systems that switch the genetic machine on and off could lead to numerous new treatments. However, the implications could spread well beyond pharmaceutical companies' balance sheets. Indeed, many analysts believe that the biotechnology revolution could transform society's economic base. During the 19th century, the industrial revolution replaced much of the developed world's traditional agricultural economic base. During the 20th century, the information revolution replaced large parts of the industrial economy. And many economists believe that during the 21st century the biotechnology revolution will largely replace the information-based economy (Greener, 2000a). While this may overstate the case, there's no doubt that genomics will form an increasingly important part of most pharmaceutical company's balance sheets.

## Japan and the Far East

Japan is one of the seven main pharmaceutical markets. However, the pharmaceutical industry is less important to the Japanese economy than in many other parts of the developed world. Nevertheless, many Japanese companies are now moving into other markets. It is therefore worth looking briefly at how the Japanese market developed.

As in Europe and American, Japanese traditional healers could draw on a rich herbal heritage. For example, the *Genroku-Sekenbanashi-Fubunshu*, consisting of 11 volumes written between 1694 and 1703, includes spells to cure or prevent illness, curious sicknesses, disease origins, medicinal plants and crude drugs, medical books, doctors and surgeons, persons who lived long and so on (Hamada, 1996). Moreover, during the 17th century the Dutch East India Company traded with Japan, bringing santalum, musk, styrax and katechu into Japan and exporting tea, Japanese camphor and moxa. There seemed to be a considerable demand for such products – for example, the accounts for 1747 include 42 medicines (Potzsch, 1998, p. 64).

During the 19th century, the increasingly open Japanese market accepted western medicines. Moreover, the Japanese government introduced medical law and regulations in 1883. Indeed, most Japanese physicians changed from eastern (*Kanpooi*) to western (*Seiyooi*) medicine. The first Japanese pharmaceutical company was established in 1885, followed by many others, which often converted from wholesalers. In some cases, these tackled Japanese problems, such as beriberi, although they also made important scientific advances, such as the isolation of adrenaline in 1900 (Yamakawa, 1995a).

However, the Japanese pharmaceutical industry began to play on the international stage during the country's reconstruction following the Second World War. The US occupation forces supported production of penicillin, although Japanese pharmaceutical companies imported many drugs and technologies from the US and Europe. This helped fuel the industry's rapid expansion between 1956 and 1970 – many companies grew at 15–20% annually (Yamakawa, 1995b). During the 1970s, the industry faced increasing regulation but still developed numerous world-class agents (Yamakawa, 1995b; see box).

Until recently, these drugs were licensed out – famotidine to Merck Sharp & Dohme, for example. However, several Japanese companies are now using these innovations to help drive their worldwide expansion. Fujisawa, for example, is using tacrolimus (Prograf) – used to prevent the rejection of transplanted organs and, in the future, serious eczema – to fund its expansion in Europe and the US. Incidentally, tacrolimus is a good example of how natural sources still lead to global medicines. Tacrolimus is derived from a microbe called *Streptomyces tsukubaensis*, named after Mount Tsukuba, the source of the soil sample in which it was found.

Advertising also developed in Japan along the same lines as in anglophone countries. In the 18th century, the paper packaging used to protect medicines from an imaginary gaseous medium, *ki* (atmospheric moisture), was printed with the brand name and indications (Hattori, 1991). Advertising expanded rapidly with radio and televisions – although in the 1960s, pharmaceutical companies were criticised for over-promoting and improperly using medicines (Takehara and Yamada, 1999).

---

**Some recent drugs from the Japanese pharmaceutical industry**

Calcium antagonists – diltiazem, nicardipine

$H_2$-blockers – famotidine.

Immunosuppressants – tacrolimus

Lipid lowerer – pravastatin

New quinolones (antibiotics) – norfloxacin, ofloxacin, etc.

---

## Dramatic differences

Despite being the second largest pharmaceutical market, there are dramatic differences between Japan and North America and Europe. In some ways, the Japanese market is less well developed than many of the other main markets. In the late 1990s, for example, the psychotropic drugs available in Japan were those used in the US during the early 1980s. Few 'new-generation' psychotropics had been approved. The antidepressants – fluoxetine, fluvoxamine, paroxetine, sertraline, venlafaxine, nefazodone – as well the antipsychotics clozapine and olanzapine are among the drugs still not approved in Japan in 1999, despite being mainstays of management in the west (Kanba, 1999).

Kanba notes: 'As a knowledge-intensive industry that conserves resources, the pharmaceutical industry would appear to be well suited to the Japanese business environment'. Yet drug-development work that would be completed in 1–2 years overseas often takes 5 or more years in Japan. As a result, Japanese pharmaceutical companies often license out the development of drugs they invented to an overseas company. For example, Sankyo Seiyaku developed donepezil, developed to treat Alzheimer's disease. By 1999, it was still in phase III clinical trials in Japan but had been launched in several other countries worldwide (Kanba, 1999).

Several reasons contribute to Japanese companies' underperformance. Clinical trials have been fraught with methodological problems, ranging from insufficient informed consent through short observation periods to poorly defined endpoints, and so on. This slowed development times in Japan and meant that the studies were not appropriate for use in other markets. The International Conference of Harmonisation (ICH) and, in particular, the rigours of Good Clinical Practice (GCP), implemented in 1997 (Ono and Kodama, 2000), should help overcome these methodological problems by ensuring that clinicians stick to rigid protocols (see Chapter 5). However, currently many clinicians feel unable to match clinical and research work – especially as among 'the academic medical community, the status of clinical research is lower than that of basic research' (Kanba, 1999). Nevertheless, Asia is increasingly moving towards the regulatory and market dynamics seen in America and Europe (Shahi and Cunningham, 1999).

## Conclusion

Despite the widely held impression that the industry is in crisis, many of the main issues are nothing new. Medicine manufacturers have faced concerns about quality and side-effects and debates about cost versus benefit since Greek and Roman times. Regulation emerged as a force in the Middle Ages and mergers have helped to drive the industry's expansion over the last 150 years. What is new, perhaps, as we enter the new millennium is science's ever-greater sophistication – typified by the Human Genome Project – which offers unpredicted opportunity for the development of new, more effective and better-tolerated medicines. On the other hand, pressure from healthcare purchasers and from the stock market conspires to threaten companies' profitability. The game may be the same: but the stakes are higher than ever.

# Chapter 2: The pharmaceutical industry's vital statistics

The international pharmaceutical industry has come a long way since its humble origins in the back rooms of chemists' shops and the laboratories of dye manufacturers. It is now a major employer and makes a major contribution to the economy of many countries. For example, according to the Association of the British Pharmaceutical Industry (ABPI), the UK's pharmaceutical sector employs around 300,000 people and generates £4.5bn towards the UK's gross domestic product (GDP). Nevertheless, the pharmaceutical industry is less important in relative terms in other leading economies, notably Japan. Japan – with 107 companies in the 1999 *Fortune* Global 500 – is second only to the US in global industrial muscle. Yet none of the leading Japanese companies are pharmaceutical companies. Against this background, this chapter summarises some of the pharmaceutical industry's vital statistics.

## A major industry?

The pharmaceutical industry presents itself as a major industrial player. This is clearly true. But how does the pharmaceutical industry compare to other sectors? Perhaps not as highly as you might expect.

For example, Merck & Co., the largest pharmaceutical company in the 1999 listings, only ranked 100 in the *Fortune* Global 500. Table 2.1 shows the world top 15 companies in all sectors. As you can see from Table 2.2, the combined revenue of the 14 pharmaceutical companies is $258,850m. The combined revenue of Wal-Mart and General Motors alone, the top two companies, is $343,367m. In other words, Wal-Mart's and General Motors' sales are some $84,517m more than the total generated by all 14 pharmaceutical companies. (However, it is worth mentioning that the pharmaceutical industry contributes to merchandisers' success. Sales of pharmaceutical products by food stores and mass merchandisers grew by 22.4% and 16.0% between 1996 and 1997.) Moreover, the pharmaceutical sector has relatively low assets per employee. Of the 34 industrial sectors in the *Fortune Global* 500, pharmaceuticals ranks 19th at $372,533.

On the other hand, despite its recent problems, pharmaceuticals ranks top in the return on assets at 14.7%, compared to, for example, 11.1% for beverages and 8% for tobacco, ranked second and third respectively. Motor vehicles ranks 19th at 2.2% and trading at 0.4% (although the Asian economic crisis in 1999/2000 probably influenced the latter's relatively poor performance.) So, it seems that the pharmaceutical sector punches above its weight, at least in terms on the return on assets.

## The largest drug companies

The *Fortune* global 500 ranking does not take the latest spate of mega-mergers into account. So, who are the main players likely to be once the mega-mergers are approved? Commerzbank recently ranked the top 20 companies (Table 2.3).

### Table 2.1: The largest 15 global companies in all sectors

| Global rank | Company | Country | Sector | Revenue ($m) | Profits ($m) |
|---|---|---|---|---|---|
| 1 | General Motors | US | Motor vehicles | 176,558.0 | 6,002.0 |
| 2 | Wal-Mart Stores | US | General merchandisers | 166,809.0 | 5,377.0 |
| 3 | Exxon Mobil | US | Petroleum refining | 163,881.0 | 7,910.0 |
| 4 | Ford Motor | US | Motor vehicles | 162,558.0 | 7,237.0 |
| 5 | Daimler Chrysler | Germany | Motor vehicles | 159,958.7 | 6,129.1 |
| 6 | Mitsui | Japan | Trading | 118,555.2 | 320.5 |
| 7 | Mitsubishi | Japan | Trading | 117,765.6 | 233.7 |
| 8 | Toyota Motor | Japan | Motor vehicles | 115,670.9 | 3,653.4 |
| 9 | General Electric | US | Diversified financials | 111,630.0 | 10,717.0 |
| 10 | Itochu | Japan | Trading | 109,068.9 | (792.8) |
| 11 | Royal Dutch/ Shell Group | UK/ Netherlands | Petroleum refining | 105,366.0 | 8,584.0 |
| 12 | Sumitomo | Japan | Trading | 95,701.6 | 314.9 |
| 13 | Nippon Telegraph & Telephone | Japan | Telecommunications | 93,591.7 | (609.0) |
| 14 | Marubeni | Japan | Trading | 91,807.4 | 18.5 |
| 15 | AXA | France | Insurance | 87,645.7 | 2,155.8 |

Figures in parentheses indicate losses

### Table 2.2 Pharmaceutical companies in the *Fortune* global 500

| Sector (global) ranking | Company | Country | Revenue ($m) | Profits ($m) | Chief executive |
|---|---|---|---|---|---|
| 1 (100) | Merck & Co. | US | 32,714 | 5,891 | Raymond Gilmartin |
| 2 (126) | Johnson & Johnson | US | 27,471 | 4,167 | Ralph Larsen |
| 3 (192) | Novartis | Switzerland | 21,609 | 4,432 | Daniel Vasella |
| 4 (206) | Bristol-Myers Squibb | US | 20,222 | 4,167 | Charles Heimbold |
| 5 (237) | AstraZeneca | UK | 18,445 | 1,143 | Tom McKillop |
| 6 (239) | Roche Group | Switzerland | 18,349 | 3,837 | Franz Humer |
| 7 (285) | Pfizer | US | 16,204 | 3,179 | William Steere Jr |
| 8 (349) | Glaxo Wellcome | UK | 13,738 | 2,930 | Robert Ingram |
| 9 (356) | SmithKline Beecham | UK | 13,562 | 1,704 | Jean-Pierre Garnier |
| 10 (358) | American Home Products | US | 13,550 | (1,227) | John Stafford |
| 11 (362) | Aventis | France | 13,438 | (1,035) | Jürgen Dormann |
| 12 (372) | Abbot Laboratories | US | 13,178 | 2,446 | Miles White |
| 13 (381) | Warner-Lambert | US | 12,929 | 1,733 | William Steere Jr |
| 14 (485) | Eli Lilly | US | 10,003 | 2,721 | Sidney Taurel |

Figures in parentheses indicate losses

## Table 2.3: The top 20 pharmaceutical companies

| Rank | Company | Market share (%) | Market capitalisation (Euro) |
|---|---|---|---|
| 1 | Glaxo Wellcome/SmithKline Beecham | 7.1 | 185,458 |
| 2 | Pfizer/Warner-Lambert | 6.9 | 313,859 |
| 3 | Merck & Co | 4.9 | 169,636 |
| 4 | AstraZeneca | 4.6 | 84,333 |
| 5 | Bristol-Myers Squibb | 4.1 | 117,905 |
| 6 | Aventis | 4.0 | 56,537 |
| 7 | Novartis | 4.0 | 108,204 |
| 8 | Johnson & Johnson | 3.6 | 144,687 |
| 9 | Roche | 3.2 | 100,468 |
| 10 | Pharmacia & Upjohn/Monsanto | 3.1 | 76,499 |
| 11 | Eli Lilly | 3.0 | 116,090 |
| 12 | American Home Products | 3.0 | 81,626 |
| 13 | Abbott Laboratories | 2.6 | 70,898 |
| 14 | Schering-Plough | 2.4 | 72,899 |
| 15 | Bayer | 1.8 | 31,295 |
| 16 | Boehringer Ingelheim | 1.4 | Not quoted |
| 17 | Takeda Chemical | 1.3 | 56,999 |
| 18 | Sanofi-Synthélabo | 1.3 | 36,686 |
| 19 | Amgen | 1.0 | 84,365 |
| 20 | Schering AG | 1.0 | 12,161 |

Source: Commerzbank

## Table 2.4: Leading drug companies by region: Japan

| Company | Rank 1999 Japan | World | Human pharmaceutical sales $bn | 1999/98 (%) | Total sales (%) |
|---|---|---|---|---|---|
| Takeda Chemical | 1 | 17 | 4.9 | 3 | 71 |
| Sankyo Pharmaceutical | 2 | 19 | 3.4 | −1 | 68 |
| Yamanouchi Pharmaceutical | 3 | 21 | 3.1 | −12 | 86 |
| Shionogi | 4 | 23 | 2.7 | 10 | 89 |
| Fujisawa Pharmaceutical | 5 | 29 | 2.0 | −6 | 87 |
| Eisai | 6 | 30 | 2.0 | −5 | 83 |
| Chugai Pharmaceutical | 7 | 34 | 1.3 | 2 | 85 |
| Daiichi Pharmaceutical | 8 | 35 | 1.3 | 2 | 55 |
| Tanebe Seiyaku | 9 | 36 | 1.2 | −8 | 78 |
| Kyowa Hakko | 10 | 38 | 1.1 | −3 | 34 |
| **Total selected companies** | | | **23.0** | **−2** | **72** |

Total sales (%) = percentage of human pharmaceutical sales in total company sales.

Source: Informa Pharmaceuticals/Philip White/Company reports

Together these account for just over 64% of the world market. Tables 2.4–2.6 show the leading drug companies – those that generate at least a billion dollars in sales – by region: Japan, US and Europe

## R&D expenditure

To maintain their position in the highly competitive global and regional rankings, drug companies invest heavily in R&D. Indeed, R&D investment is higher in pharmaceuticals than in most other sectors. In the large pharmaceutical companies, R&D consumes between 15% and 18% of sales. Marketing and sales account for between 30% and 35% (James, 2000). Smaller companies' R&D spend varies between 10% and 18% of sales, depending on the number of expensive phase III clinical trials under way (page 66). As most large pharmaceutical companies have several phase III studies under way at any one time, the proportion of their sales invested in R&D remains relatively constant.

### Table 2.5: Leading drug companies by region: US

| Company | Rank 1999 US | Rank 1999 World | Human pharmaceutical sales $bn | Human pharmaceutical sales 1999/98 (±%) | Total sales (%) |
|---|---|---|---|---|---|
| Pfizer & Warner-Lambert | 1 | 2 | 23.3 | 21 | 84 |
| Merck & Co. | 2 | 3 | 17.5 | 14 | 53 |
| Bristol-Myers Squibb | 3 | 5 | 14.3 | 14 | 71 |
| Johnson & Johnson | 4 | 8 | 12.0 | 18 | 44 |
| American Home Products | 5 | 12 | 10.5 | 10 | 78 |
| Pharmacia Corporation | 6 | 10 | 10.1 | 23 | 62 |
| Eli Lilly | 7 | 11 | 9.4 | 9 | 94 |
| Schering-Plough | 8 | 14 | 8.3 | 15 | 90 |
| Abbott Laboratories | 9 | 13 | 5.0 | 0 | 38 |

Total sales (%) = percentage of human pharmaceutical sales in total company sales.

Source: Informa Pharmaceuticals/Philip White/Company reports

### Table 2.6: Leading drug companies by region: Europe

| Company | Rank 1999 Europe | Rank 1999 World | Human pharmaceutical sales $bn | Human pharmaceutical sales 1999/98 (±%) | Total sales (%) |
|---|---|---|---|---|---|
| Glaxo SmithKline | 1 | 1 | 24.5 | 8 | 90 |
| Glaxo Wellcome | | | 13.8 | 5 | 100 |
| SmithKline Beecham | | | 10.8 | 11 | 79 |
| Aventis | 2 | 6 | 14.9 | 7 | 68 |
| AstraZeneca | 3 | 4 | 14.7 | 35 | 80 |
| Novartis | 4 | 7 | 14.0 | 9 | 65 |
| Roche | 5 | 9 | 11.0 | 15 | 60 |
| Bayer | 6 | 15 | 7.2 | 13 | 24 |

Total sales (%) = percentage of human pharmaceutical sales in total company sales.

Source: Informa Pharmaceuticals/Philip White/Company reports

However, this level of investment is a relatively recent development. During the 1930s, pharmaceutical companies were 'middling R&D spenders'. By the 1970s, however, R&D spend by the drug industry was among the highest in any manufacturing sector (Edgerton, 1966, p. 34). This trend continued over the next few years as science played a growing role in development and because of the regulatory restrictions introduced in the wake of the thalidomide tragedy. Trends in UK R&D expenditure illustrate both the marked growth in absolute terms as well as the increasing proportion of all industrial R&D accounted for by the pharmaceutical sector (Table 2.7). Tables 2.8–2.10 show the leading companies' R&D expenditure by region, while Table 2.11 shows different countries' success at coming up with new products. As we see in Chapter 9, the UK is also the European leader in biotechnology R&D.

#### Table 2.7: Trends in UK R&D expenditure

| Year | R&D expenditure (£m) | R&D as % of output | R&D as % of all industry R&D |
|---|---|---|---|
| 1972 | 42 | 7 | 5 |
| 1985 | 546 | 14 | 11 |
| 1990 | 1,140 | 17 | 14 |
| 1991 | 1,239 | 17 | 15 |
| 1992 | 1,420 | 17 | 17 |
| 1993 | 1,707 | 21 | 19 |
| 1994 | 1,918 | 20 | 21 |
| 1995 | 1,903 | 19 | 21 |
| 1996 | 2,078 | 20 | 22 |
| 1997 | 2,251 | 21 | 23 |
| 1998 | 2,375 | NA | 23 |
| 1999 | 2,700 | NA | NA |

NA = Not available.

Source: ABPI

#### Table 2.8: Leading drug companies' R&D expenditure: Japan

| Company | R&D spend 1999 ($m) | % sales (total) | % sales (human pharmaceuticals) | % change over 1998 |
|---|---|---|---|---|
| Takeda Chemical | 640 | 9.2 | 13.0 | −2 |
| Sankyo Pharmaceutical | 517 | 10.2 | 15.0 | 11 |
| Yamanouchi Pharmaceutical | 449 | 12.8 | 15.0 | 24 |
| Eisai | 361 | 15.3 | 18.5 | −3 |
| Fujisawa Pharmaceutical | 346 | 15.1 | 17.3 | 1 |
| Daiichi Pharmaceutical | 317 | 13.3 | 24.1 | 6 |
| Chugai Pharmaceutical | 311 | 19.8 | 23.4 | 5 |
| Shionogi | 218 | 7.1 | 8.0 | 4 |
| Kyowa Hakko | 199 | 6.3 | 18.6 | −5 |
| Tanabe Seiyaku | 164 | 10.4 | 13.3 | −2 |

Source: Company reports

### Table 2.9: Leading drug companies' R&D expenditure: US

| Company | R&D spend 1999 ($m) | % sales (total) | % sales (human pharmaceuticals) | % change over 1998 |
|---|---|---|---|---|
| Pfizer & Warner-Lambert | 4,035 | 14.6 | 17.3 | 22 |
| Pharmacia Corporation | 2,189 | 13.3 | 21.7 | 12 |
| Merck & Co. | 2,068 | 6.3 | 11.8 | 14 |
| Eli Lilly | 1,784 | 17.8 | 19.0 | 3 |
| Bristol-Myers Squibb | 1,646 | 8.1 | 11.5 | 18 |
| Johnson & Johnson | 1,600 | 5.8 | 13.4 | 13 |
| American Home Products | 1,500 | 11.1 | 14.2 | 8 |
| Abbott Laboratories | 1,194 | 9.1 | 23.9 | -3 |
| Schering Plough | 1,191 | 13.0 | 14.3 | 18 |

Source: Informa Pharmaceuticals/Philip White/Company reports

### Table 2.10: Leading drug companies' R&D expenditure: Europe

| Company | R&D spend 1999 ($m) | % sales (total) | % sales (human pharmaceuticals) | % change over 1998 |
|---|---|---|---|---|
| Glaxo SmithKline | 3,568 | 13.1 | 14.6 | 10 |
| Glaxo Wellcome | 2,056 | 14.9 | 14.9 | 9 |
| SmithKline Beecham | 1,512 | 11.1 | 14.0 | 11 |
| Aventis | 2,604 | 11.9 | 17.5 | |
| AstraZeneca | 2,454 | 13.3 | 16.7 | 13 |
| Roche | 2,032 | 11.1 | 18.5 | 11 |
| Navartis | 1,899 | 8.8 | 13.6 | 9 |
| Bayer | 1,017 | 3.5 | 14.2 | 24 |

Source: Informa Pharmaceuticals/Philip White/Company reports

### Table 2.11: Estimated product pipelines for top 40 companies worldwide in 1997, by nationality

| Country | Estimated product pipelines |
|---|---|
| UK | 31 |
| Switzerland | 29 |
| US | 24 |
| France | 19 |
| Japan | 16 |
| Germany | 15 |
| Denmark | 10 |
| Netherlands | 7 |
| **Average** | **20.43** |

Source: IMS/ ABPI

## The top 10 pharmaceutical markets

While the pharmaceutical industry is truly global, reaching into the developing as well as the developed world, the top 10 pharmaceutical markets (Table 2.12) accounted for some 84% of the total global market in 1998. However, the per capita expenditure on medicines varies widely within these markets (Table 2.13). The other markets are much less important. To illustrate this, Table 2.14 shows a breakdown of Bayer's sales and earnings by region in 1999.

### Table 2.12 The top 10 pharmaceutical markets 1998

| Rank | Country | 1998 sales ($bn) | % of global sales |
|---|---|---|---|
| 1 | US[a] | 99.5 | 39.6 |
| 2 | Japan[a] | 38.8 | 15.4 |
| 3 | Germany[a] | 18.2 | 7.2 |
| 4 | France | 14.1 | 5.6 |
| 5 | Italy[a] | 10.9 | 4.3 |
| 6 | UK[a] | 10.2 | 4.1 |
| 7 | Brazil | 6.5 | 2.6 |
| 8 | Spain | 5.3 | 2.1 |
| 9 | Canada[a] | 4.9 | 1.9 |
| 10 | Argentina | 3.6 | 1.4 |

[a] Includes hospital sales.

Source: IMS Health/*PharmaBusiness* (1999)

### Table 2.13: Per capita sales of pharmaceuticals in major markets 1999

| Country | Pharmaceutical sales per person (£) |
|---|---|
| US | 251 |
| Japan | 210 |
| France | 183 |
| Belgium | 156 |
| Switzerland | 143 |
| Germany | 140 |
| Sweden | 134 |
| Austria | 125 |
| Italy | 116 |
| UK | 107 |
| Spain | 95 |
| Netherlands | 90 |

Source: ABPI/ IMS

**Table 2.14: Proportion of Bayer's sales and earnings by region 1999**

| Region | Sales (%) | Earnings (%) |
|---|---|---|
| Asia/Africa/Australia | 18 | 8 |
| Latin America | 8 | 3 |
| North America | 30 | 14 |
| Europe | 44 | 75 |

Source: Commerzbank

Moreover, most major markets are growing rapidly, especially if you take a long-term view. In the UK, for example, the medicines market was worth £94m in 1960. This increased to £241m in 1970, £1246m in 1980 and £3610m in 1990. By 1997, the UK medicine market was worth around £6904m. And the UK is one of the most conservative and among the highest users of generics of any of the major markets (source: ABPI). All this makes the pharmaceutical sector a tempting investment opportunity for stock markets.

## Employees

As mentioned above, pharmaceutical companies are major employers in many countries. The European-based companies with sales over $1bn employ 0.7m people, for example. The sector is a major employer even in Japan, where, as we have seen, the sector is of less importance to the country's economy than in Europe or America. In the mid-1990s, Japanese hospitals accounted for almost 60% of ethical sales, three times the UK proportion. As a result, Japanese pharmaceutical company sales representatives make few detail calls to GPs, entrusting these to wholesalers' representatives. However, at this time, pharmaceutical companies and wholesalers employed 86,000 sales representative – equivalent to one sales representative for every 2.3 doctors (Macarthur, 1995). Indeed, most major players make a major investment in their sales force, despite the growth of new media and the emergence of new stakeholders (Table 2.15). Table 2.16 shows the top 30 companies ranked by number of employees.

## The blockbusters

Increasingly, large companies need the mature sales (see Life cycle, page 86) generated by several blockbusters – drugs that achieve sales of more than $1bn annually – to fund R&D programmes and meet shareholders' expectations of growth. Indeed, increasingly companies gear their R&D programmes to discover the next blockbuster, rather than considering smaller areas of unmet need. This has left a gap that smaller companies can fill.

Certainly, blockbusters can be important to a company's success. Takeda Abbott Pharmaceuticals (TAP), for example, is a joint venture formed by Takeda Chemical and Abbott Laboratories that operates only in the US. Nevertheless, sales in 1999 ranked 11th in the US and 22nd in the world. Yet, TAP sells just two drugs – the proton pump inhibitor (PPI) Prevacid (lansoperazole) and Leupron (leuprolide) for prostate cancer and endometriosis. Prevacid was the fourth

## Table 2.15: Size of leading pharmaceutical companies' sales forces

| Company | Sales force |
|---|---|
| Pfizer/Warner-Lambert | 8,200 |
| Glaxo/SmithKline | 7,200 |
| Pfizer | 5,500 |
| Johnson & Johnson | 5,000 |
| Merck & Co. | 4,700 |
| Schering-Plough | 4,300 |
| Bristol-Myers Squibb | 4,300 |
| Glaxo Wellcome | 4,200 |
| Aventis | 4,000 |
| Pharmacia & Upjohn/Monsanto | 3,800 |
| AstraZeneca | 3,400 |
| Novartis | 3,200 |
| SmithKline Beecham | 3,000 |
| Eli Lilly | 3,000 |
| American Home Products | 3,000 |
| Warner-Lambert | 2,700 |
| Roche | 2,400 |
| Searle | 2,000 |
| Bayer | 1,700 |

Source: Commerzbank

## Table 2.16: Top 30 companies ranked by number of employees

| Rank | Company | Employees 1998 | Rank | Company | Employees 1998 |
|---|---|---|---|---|---|
| 1 | Nestlé | 231,881 | 16 | American Home Products | 52,984 |
| 2 | Aventis Pharma[a] | 162,147 | 17 | AstraZeneca[b] | > 50,000 |
| 3 | Bayer Group | 120,400 | 18 | Pfizer | 46,000 |
| 4 | Procter & Gamble | > 110,000 | 19 | Warner Lambert | 41,000 |
| 5 | BASF Group | 105,945 | 20 | Baxter International | 41,000 |
| 6 | Johnson & Johnson | 93,100 | 21 | Sanofi-Synthélabo[c] | 38,492 |
| 7 | Akzo Nobel | 85,900 | 22 | Solvay | 33,104 |
| 8 | Novartis | 82,449 | 23 | Pharmacia & Upjohn | > 30,000 |
| 9 | 3M | 76,509 | 24 | Monsanto | > 30,000 |
| 10 | Roche Holding | 66,707 | 25 | Eli Lilly | 29,843 |
| 11 | SmithKline Beecham | 58,300 | 26 | Merck KGaA | 28,911 |
| 12 | Merck & Co. | 57,300 | 27 | Boehringer Ingelheim | 25,927 |
| 13 | Abbott Laboratories | 56,000 | 28 | Schering-Plough | 25,100 |
| 14 | Glaxo Wellcome | 54,350 | 29 | Schering AG | 21,800 |
| 15 | Bristol-Myers Squibb | > 54,000 | 30 | Takeda Chemical Co. | 16,443 |

[a] Before merger: Rhône-Poulenc = 65,180, Hoechst Group = 96,967. [b] Before merger: Zeneca = 34,600, Astra = 24,958. [c] Before merger: Sanofi =29,621, Synthélabo = 8,871.

Source: various/company websites

biggest selling drug in the US during 1999 (17th worldwide in 1998). These two products made TAP the fastest growing of the American pharmaceutical companies with sales over $1bn. Similarly, epoetin alpha made a major contribution to the success of both Amgen, who discovered the drug, and Johnson & Johnson who license it for specific indications. Without wanting to labour the point, it is worth mentioning that Pfizer is currently one of the most successful pharmaceutical companies. Given that Pfizer sells six blockbusters, this success is perhaps not surprising.

In 1998, 30 products achieved sales of more than $1bn worldwide, making them blockbusters. Indeed, seven brands made more than $2bn, while Losec (omeprazole), for gastric ulcers, and the lipid-lowering agent Zocor (simvastatin) achieved sales of almost $4bn (Table 2.17). To make the top 100 products, a brand needs to generate at least $405m a year in sales (*PharmaBusiness,* 1999). In comparison, the average new chemical entity generates around $350m in peak sales (James, 2000).

## The rise of generic industry

As pressure on healthcare budgets worldwide continues to increase (see page 40), generic prescribing will remain a mainstay of governmental attempts to contain costs. Generic prescribing encourages doctors to write a prescription by the chemical ('generic') rather than by the brand name. In other words, a doctor writes 'omeprazole' rather than 'Losec' and 'fluoxetine' rather than 'Prozac'. The pharmacist is then free to dispense the cheapest version of the drug that is available. In some countries, in some circumstances, pharmacists can substitute a generic on their own initiative (generic substitution). Critics, however, note that some brands differ in their pharmacodynamic or pharmacokinetic profile (see Chapter 5). This could leave patients vulnerable to side-effects or ineffectiveness. As a result, exceptions to the generic prescribing rule are made for some medications – such as antiepileptics and when the drug delivery system is critical, e.g. in some treatments for asthma and high blood pressure.

When the patent protecting a drug expires, any company can manufacture a generic version provided it meets relevant regulatory requirements concerning, for example, their manufacturing facilities. These 'generic houses' tend to have much lower overheads than conventional companies. For instance, generic houses do not invest heavily in either R&D or a large marketing and sales department. So they have less of an investment to seek a return on and can price the drug much lower than the branded version. As a result, generic competition poses a major issue for healthcare companies worldwide. Between 2000 and 2005, almost a third of the sales of the top ten drug companies will be against generic competition (James, 2000). But, as we'll see, companies are beginning to explore ways to minimise any possible damage from generics.

Worldwide, many countries introduced incentives to prescribe generically (see Chapter 3). And these seem to have worked. In the UK, for example, the *Health and Personal Social Service Statistics for England 1999* reveal that 48% of prescriptions were written generically in 1998, up 7% from 1994. Nevertheless, the size of the generics market in absolute terms as well as a percentage of the total varies considerably. Table 2.18 shows the size of generic markets in 13 European countries and the proportion of the total accounted for by generics.

## Table 2.17: Drugs with sales of more than $1bn during 1998

| Rank | Brand name | Generic name | Drug class | Main clinical area | Sales ($bn) |
|---|---|---|---|---|---|
| 1 | Losec | Omeprazole | PPI | Ulcer healing | 3.98 |
| 2 | Zocor | Simvastatin | Statin | Lipid regulation | 3.95 |
| 3 | Prozac | Fluoxetine | SSRI | Depression, etc | 2.81 |
| 4 | Norvasc | Amlodipine | CCB | Hypertension, angina | 2.58 |
| 5 | Renitec | Enalapril | ACE inhibitor | Hypertension, heart failure | 2.40 |
| 6 | Claritin | Loratadine | Antihistamine | Hay fever and other allergy | 2.30 |
| 7 | Lipitor | Atorvastatin | Statin | Lipid regulation | 2.20 |
| 8 | Zoloft | Sertraline | SSRI | Depression, etc | 1.84 |
| 9 | Seroxat | Paroxetine | SSRI | Depression, etc | 1.76 |
| 10 | Premarin/ Premphase/ Prempro | Oestrogen with and without progestogen | Sex hormone | HRT | 1.65 |
| 11 | Lipostat | Pravastatin | Statin | Lipid regulation | 1.64 |
| 12 | Augmentin | Co-amoxiclav | Antibiotic | Infections | 1.60 |
| 13 | Zyprexa | Olanzapine | Atypical antipsychotic | Schizophrenia | 1.44 |
| 14 | Ciproxin | Ciprofloxacin | Antibiotic | Infections | 1.40 |
| 15 | Epogen | Epoetin alfa | Erythropoietin | Anaemia in dialysis | 1.38 |
| 16 | Procrit | Epoetin alfa | Erythropoietin | Other anaemia | 1.36 |
| 17 | Prevacid | Lansoperazole | PPI | Ulcer healing | 1.35 |
| 18 | Neoral/ Sandimmun | Cyclosporin | Immuno-suppressant | Transplantation, etc | 1.28 |
| 19 | Zantac | Ranitidine | $H_2$ antagonist | Ulcer healing | 1.26 |
| 20 | Klacid | Clarithromycin | Antibiotic | Infections | 1.25 |
| 21 | Taxol | Paclitaxel | Taxane | Cancer | 1.21 |
| 22 | Rocephin | Ceftriaxone | Antibiotic | Infections | 1.18 |
| 23 | Imigran | Sumatriptan | Triptan | Migraine | 1.16 |
| 24 | Zestril | Lisinopril | ACE inhibitor | Hypertension, heart failure | 1.12 |
| 25 | Neupogen | Filgrastim | Growth factor | Neutropenia | 1.12 |
| 26 | Pepcidin | Famotidine | PPI | Ulcer healing | 1.11 |
| 27 | Voltaren-XR | Diclofenac | NSAID | Pain and inflammation | 1.08 |
| 28 | Cozaar | Losartan | ACE inhibitor | Hypertension, heart failure | 1.06 |
| 29 | Adalat | Nifedipine | CCB | Hypertension, angina | 1.05 |
| 30 | Zithromax | Azithromycin | Antibiotic | Infections | 1.04 |

Brand name in US market cited.

ACE = angiotensin converting enzyme; CCB = calcium channel blocker; HRT = hormone replacement treatment; NSAID = nonsteroidal anti-inflammatory drug; PPI = proton pump inhibitor; SSRI = selective serotonin reuptake inhibitor

Source: adapted from *PharmaBusiness*, 1999.

### Table 2.18: European generic market 1997

| Country | Generic market (Euro m) | % of whole market |
| --- | --- | --- |
| Germany | 5,165 | 38.8 |
| UK | 1,318 | 21.7 |
| France | 290 | 2.4 |
| Italy | 200 | 3.0 |
| Netherlands | 241 | 13.2 |
| Greece | 154 | 12.6 |
| Belgium | 103 | 5.9 |
| Portugal | 34 | 2.8 |
| Sweden | 63 | 4.2 |
| Austria | 95 | 8.7 |
| Denmark | 161 | 37.5 |
| Finland | 289 | 32.0 |
| Ireland | 36 | 12.7 |

Source: FT/NERA

Against this background, it is perhaps not surprising that some generic companies are beginning to emerge as major players. For example, Canadian Bernard Sherman founded the generic company Apotex in 1974. Sales in 1999 reached $500m. Furthermore, Norton, which began as a predominantly generic house, is now the UK's third largest asthma company.

Although standard price indices may not accurately show the cost to the health service (Gerdtham *et al.*, 1998), as they fail to allow for discounts and so on, the savings offered by genetics may be large. Some generics undercut the under-patent prices by up to 90%. Overall, generics reduce the average product price by 50% in the US and 42%, 36% and 25% in Germany, the UK and Canada respectively. However, generic competition reduced prices by just 16% in France and 6% in Japan. In Italy, however, generic competition was associated with a 5% price *increase*. This may reflect the fact that, in Italy and Japan, generics tend to be marketed by licensed comarketers rather than true generic houses. Such companies are unlikely to have much incentive to cut costs (Danzon and Chao, 2000).

## Production

As discussed in Chapter 6, pharmaceutical manufacturing is now a worldwide business. It is more cost-effective to consolidate production by brand and formulation rather than to fragment manufacturing in factories spread across the world. Nevertheless, pharmaceutical production is concentrated in a few countries. Indeed, the top five countries account for more than 80% of the world's pharmaceutical production (Table 2.19). For example, tacrolimus is manufactured in bulk in Japan but formulated and packaged into Prograf in Eire. From here, it is shipped worldwide.

### Table 2.19: World pharmaceutical production in 1997

| Country | Production value (£m) | % of total |
|---|---|---|
| US | 58,951.2 | 37.6 |
| Japan | 30,800.0 | 19.7 |
| France | 13,103.0 | 8.4 |
| Germany | 12,298.8 | 7.8 |
| UK | 10,422.1 | 6.7 |
| Italy | 7,239.1 | 4.6 |
| Switzerland | 6,813.6 | 4.3 |
| Canada | 2,469.1 | 1.6 |
| Sweden | 2,270.5 | 1.4 |
| Belgium | 2,233.3 | 1.4 |
| Netherlands | 1,345.6 | 0.9 |
| Others | 4,908.6 | 3.1 |

Source: ABPI

## Industry organisations

Pharmaceutical companies operate in one of the most tightly regulated and politically sensitive of any industrial sector. Pharmaceutical companies contend with local and international regulatory requirements that dramatically restrict their products' availability – in most cases the end-user cannot even buy the product. And they still have to work against the backdrop of international free trade agreements.

As a result, the industry needs a means to engage politicians and the public in, for example, discussions of the ethical dimensions to pharmaceutical science as well as to lobby effectively at both national and transnational levels. Against this background, pharmaceutical companies formed industry organisations to better represent their views. While many sectors have trade organisations, the pharmaceutical industry bodies are among the most vocal, reflecting the considerable pressures facing the sector.

For example, in the US, the Pharmaceutical Research and Manufacturers of America (PhRMA) represents the leading research-based pharmaceutical and biotechnology companies. The Australian Pharmaceutical Manufacturers Association (APMA) and the Association of the British Pharmaceutical Industry (ABPI) perform similar tasks in Australia and the UK. There are similar organisations in other parts of the world.

Moreover, as the sector increasingly embraced globalisation, so did the industrial associations. The International Federation of Pharmaceutical Manufacturers Associations (IFPMA) represents the worldwide research-based pharmaceutical industry and manufacturers of prescription medicines. The IFPMA facilitates the exchange of information within the international industry and helps develop international policy. Moreover, the IFPMA is the main conduit for the pharmaceutical sector to work with transnational organisations such as the World Health Organization, the World Bank, the World Trade Organization and the World Intellectual Property Organization (see Chapter 8).

## Drug companies' other interests

Many drugs companies have interests outside core ethical pharmaceuticals. One recent merger, for example, was between Pharmacia & Upjohn and Monsanto, best known for its pioneering work with genetically modified food. (However, Monsanto will be a stand-alone company with publicly traded stock.)

In many ways, a business model based more broadly on life sciences or chemicals is sensible. Many products of pharmaceutical research apply equally to animal health and human disease, the controversial use of antibiotics in food production being an obvious example. Moreover, many chemical processes have other applications. The expertise a company gains through developing enzymes for therapeutic use may also allow it to manufacture enzymes for food production or even for use in soap powders. And, of course, some of today's leading pharmaceutical companies, especially those in Japan and Europe, originally began life as broad-based chemical companies.

As a result, several large drug companies have interests other than medicines. Novo Nordisk, a world leader in insulin and diabetes care, is also the world's largest producer of enzymes for industrial use, for example. Their products are used in washing powders, toothpastes, contact lens cleaners, baking and brewing, and so on. In 1999, the enzyme business generated sales of DK4501m, around a quarter of the healthcare sales (DK16,423m).

Some other major pharmaceutical companies – such as Bayer, Aventis and Novartis – have a long history in agrochemicals. Roche, Bayer and more recently Warner-Lambert are active in the vitamin market. Roche also developed an important franchise in diagnostics, while BASF and Bayer, both German companies, remain traditional conglomerates spanning a wide range of chemical manufacture.

Many companies – such as SmithKline Beecham – also have active over-the-counter (OTC) sales divisions, despite the fact that profitability in this area is traditionally lower than in prescription sales. Increasingly, companies consider OTC switching as offering one way of maintaining sales towards the end of the life cycle (see page 86). In many cases, drugs have acquired sufficient use under close medical supervision to allow their use by patients purchasing the agent from a pharmacist.

However, the relative commercial importance of the areas of pharmaceutical company's interests varies depending on region and company. For example:

- In Japan, some 72% of sales from the 10 companies with pharmaceutical revenues over $1bn during 1999 came from human therapeutic pharmaceuticals. Nevertheless, Daiichi obtains some 45% of its sales from diagnostics, radiologicals and fine chemicals. Moreover, some 66% of Kyowa Hakko's revenues come from liquor, food and bulk chemicals. Kyowa Hakko, in common with many other Japanese companies, retains its bulk chemical manufacturing capability despite the sector's current unprofitability.

- Overall, among the US-based companies with sales over $1bn in 1999, around 66% of revenues comes from human therapeutic pharmaceuticals. Pfizer, Eli Lilly and Schering-Plough generate more than 80% of their turnover from this source. On the other hand, Abbott, Johnson & Johnson and Pharmacia rely on broader portfolios, including medical devices, diagnostics, nutrition and agrochemicals.

- Many European-based pharmaceutical companies have broader portfolios than either Japan or the US, reflecting, perhaps, the historical importance of dye manufacturers in the sector's evolution (see Chapter 1). Some 55% of the revenues of the Europe-based companies with sales over $1bn comes from human therapeutic pharmaceuticals in 1999, for example. Indeed, BASF generates sales of some $31.5bn and is a major element in the German economy, supplying plastics, oil and gas, health and nutrition, colourings, finishing products, and so on. Bayer offers agrochemicals, chemicals and polymers, as well as producing pharmaceuticals and being a world leader in diagnostics.

However, there seems to be two main strands of thought surrounding this diverse marketing approach. The first, held by Aventis and Roche, is to remain a broad-based life sciences company, exploiting synergies between areas. Certainly, as we have seen, areas other than human therapeutic pharmaceuticals can make a considerable contribution to sales, especially in Europe. The other approach is to focus on core competency of pharmaceutical manufacture. Thus, Novartis and AstraZeneca recently merged their agrochemicals business, while Novo Nordisk spun off the enzyme business into a separately listed company.

Time will tell which approach proves right over the longer term. However, both could be successful, depending on each company's historical and financial circumstances. This highlights a theme that emerges throughout this book – there is no single way to build a large company.

# Chapter 3: Market dynamics

Pharmaceutical companies pay consultants millions to predict market trends. But in broad terms, just about the only thing that a pharmaceutical company can rely on with any certainly is that the market conditions next year will probably not be the same they are now. Pharmaceutical markets are subject to complex dynamics the outcomes of which are often difficult to predict.

For example, governments worldwide continually fine-tune their attempts to contain costs. The growing influence of pharmaco-economics, health technology assessment organisations and treatment guidelines may advocate or reject a drug, for example. While these may not dramatically alter a market's size overall – they often favour one treatment over another – they can influence a particular manufacturer's profitability. Moreover, rival companies may introduce an alternative treatment – exclusivity periods are progressively shorter and later introductions are often cheaper. However, many of the dynamics do not influence only a single market. Globalisation means that factors and issues on one side of the world can easily influence those on the other. And if this was not enough, companies need to contend with the growing influence of nongovernmental organisations, some of which are not the traditional healthcare special interest groups.

## The drive towards globalisation

It has become almost a truism that drug companies need to become global to ensure an adequate return on investment. Indeed, several recent trends support the idea that large companies now have – or want – a global reach (Hess *et al.*, 1999):

- The recent spate of mergers and acquisitions on an international level that increase global reach

- Consolidation: as mentioned elsewhere, the top 20 companies control over 60% of the world market – the consolidation of the sector means that this trend is likely to continue

- A growing number of alliances, again to increase global presence

- A growing pressure by purchasers to control costs, supported by increased transparency and harmonisation in prices (although as we will see later, making international pricing comparisons is fraught with difficulty).

It is also a truism that regulations need to move in line with the market dynamics and, in particular, the move towards globalisation. Indeed, governments increasingly believe that transnational regulation is the only way to deal with companies' global reach as well as being a means of promoting economic and political stability. This underlies the importance that national governments attach to the European Union (EU), the World Trade Organization, the International Monetary Fund (IMF) and so on. These organisations are discussed in Chapter 8.

So, what drove the pharmaceutical industry to become global? Three factors appear to have been influential (Hess *et al.*, 1999). First, the medical community is increasingly global. Conferences, journals and, more recently, the Internet are global in scope. Moreover, there is an increasing trend among governments and health advocates to compare best practice and statistics – such as disease-related morbidity and mortality – between countries. Reaching this international audience means that marketing needs to be global, ideally with globally recognised brands. This places pharmaceutical companies in a difficult position. They need to be a global industry. But the products and service they offer must relate to healthcare needs both globally and regionally (Asia and Europe, for instance) while working within legal, regulatory and attitudinal differences in each market (although there is increasing harmonisation – see Chapter 8). While all global companies must, to a greater or lesser extent, work within the confines imposed by transnational regulation, the problems facing the pharmaceutical sector appear to be among the most difficult to solve – a theme that will recur throughout this book.

Secondly, increased integration of government regulation helps *drive* – as well as respond to – globalisation (Hess *et al.*, 1999). The European Union has a centralised regulatory system (see Chapter 8), reflecting an increasing concordance between patients, medical communities and practices across Europe. This is also, of course, part of a political agenda to harmonise trade. However, differences in reimbursement (see below) can still lead to variations in marketing. Moreover, many regulatory authorities are now willing to consider data generated in clinical trials elsewhere in the world, a trend encouraged by the global importance attached to Good Clinical Practice (GCP). This is discussed in Chapters 5 and 8.

This move towards integrated governmental regulation reduces the barriers for global firms promoting global messages and marketing global brands. However, integrated governmental regulation also leads to a fundamental paradox at the heart of globalisation – at least from the political perspective (and the pharmaceutical sector is one of the most politicised branches of industry).

On the one hand, governments call for developing counties to embrace democracy. On the other, as John Gray notes in his influential book *False Dawn: The Delusions of Global Capitalism* (1999, p. 18), the same governments believe that '[t]he rules of the game of the market must be elevated beyond any possibility of revision through democratic choice…. Transnational organisations can get away with this [encouraging free markets] only in so far as they are immune from the pressure of democratic political life.' The feeling that the regulators of global capitalism are immune to democratic pressure is one factor underlying a new global medical ethic (Chapter 10) as well as increasing political advocacy (see below) more generally. Such issues contributed to the background to Monsanto's recent merger and to recent riots at meetings of the IMF and World Bank.

Finally, most pharmaceutical companies look to a global market to maximise their return on investment. European and American companies have a long history of global marketing. The trend is therefore best exemplified by the sea change in Japanese companies' attitudes towards globalisation over recent years. Japanese companies have long been pharmaceutical innovators, developing famotidine, atorvastatin and donepezil (for gastric ulcers, raised lipid and Alzheimer's disease respectively) to name three. However, traditionally Japanese companies licensed their discoveries out. Recently, however, Japanese companies looked at their margins and decided they could maximise their return on investment by expanding rather than licensing out.

So several Japanese companies are now using their latest innovations to drive worldwide expansion. Fujisawa, for example, is using the success of the global immunosuppressant brand Prograf (tacrolimus) to drive expansion in Europe and the US. Indeed, half the sales of Prograf now come from the US. However, Yamanouchi Pharmaceutical was among the first of the big Japanese companies to dip its toe in the global waters, buying Duphar Laboratories in the Netherlands in the early 1990s.

The recognition of the value offered by a global market is not confined to Asia. Drug companies have considerable fixed costs in development, low variable production costs and focused markets. As Hess and colleagues (1999) point out, drug companies do not really market 'drugs' per se. Rather they market a specific product for specific, sometime tightly defined, conditions in highly regulated markets. So, each drug brings with it a plethora of associated values and influences. As Hess *et al.* point out this encourages globalisation. The huge costs of developing and marketing a pharmaceutical mean that a company needs to reach as many customers as possible to maximise the return on investment. This imperative is beginning to redefine the product life cycle (see page 86).

However, companies also need to be aware of local differences that could influence profitability. Some markets have different niche concerns. In the 1980s, German physicians each year managed 163 consultations per million of the population for vertigo and dizziness caused by low blood pressure – compared to none in England. There is a serious condition, known as orthostatic hypotension (a dangerous fall in blood pressure), that all doctors would treat. The German malady arises at blood pressures that American and English doctors would probably consider beneficial rather than hazardous. Nevertheless, at the time, some 85 drugs were listed for 'low blood pressure' in Germany (Payer, 1989, p. 86). Such differences could represent lucrative niche markets, especially for smaller companies sensitive to local concerns.

Moreover, global companies need to appreciate the impact of local economic factors that influence their return from that part of the world. In some countries – Indonesia for example – almost all the primary pharmaceutical is imported. This makes the health service, and therefore its suppliers, vulnerable to currency fluctuations (Shahi and Cunningham, 1999). In other words, global companies need sophisticated internal systems to assess and manage these factors.

## Stock market pressures

The stock markets' and shareholders' attitudes towards companies and the sector generally are highly influential in shaping the pharmaceutical market. Most large pharmaceutical companies need to raise revenue to fund their growth. They may raise the capital by taking out a loan either with a bank or venture capitalists. More commonly, the large companies issue shares, which are bought by stockbrokers on behalf of shareholders, institutions or pension funds. In return, investors expect the value of their shareholding to increase and to receive a dividend (share of the profits) each year.

As a result, the stock market expects the pharmaceutical sector to grow at a healthy rate. A survey of 15 analysts in 2000 found that they expected the large pharmaceutical companies to grow by between 12% and 15% per year between 2000 and 2005. They also expected sales to increase by between 8% and 10% each year, with the market increasing by between 6% and 8% annually. However, the US market – the last unfettered free pharmaceutical market – accounts for some 75% of growth worldwide, reflecting, in part, the impact of pricing controls.

Increasingly, analysts recognise the considerable gulf between 'what the industry *can* deliver and what it *wants* to achieve' (Drews, 1999). A 1995 survey suggested that, even with zero growth, there was a deficit in the top 10 companies of five new drugs a year. For the top 20 companies, the innovation deficit reached seven drugs per year. But few shareholders accept zero growth. For an average 5% growth, the deficit would be 19 substances a year, reaching 30 for a 10% growth (Drews, 1999).

Moreover, in many companies a combination of pricing restrictions and generic competition means that the major companies' existing portfolio accounts for perhaps only half the stock market's expectations for growth. Drugs in the pipeline need to make up the shortfall (James, 2000). Today, to sustain average growth rates, a company needs to launch one product with sales of around £300m per year for each 1–1.5% of the world market that the company has. This means, that a company the size of Glaxo Wellcome/SmithKline Beecham will need to launch between three and seven new products a year, while AstraZeneca needs between two and four. Overall, the pharmaceutical industry needs between 70 and 100 new products of this sales value every year to maintain growth (Horrobin, 2000).

In theory, there should be no reason why the industry cannot maintain this growth. After all, unlike many sectors, pharmaceuticals do not have to manufacture demand: the need for new products is present in every doctor's waiting room or hospital clinic. Genomics and molecular biology are coming up with a greater than ever number of possible targets. And combinatorial chemistry and high-throughput screening means that the industry can evaluate more lead compounds than ever before (see Chapter 4). Nevertheless, the number of new chemical entities reaching the market has declined sharply since the 1960s, when the global pharmaceutical industry introduced between 80 and 100 drugs a year. This fell to between 50 and 60 in the early 1980s and declined further to between 30 and 40 in the late 1990s (Horrobin, 2000). If the market suspects that the expected growth from drugs in the pipeline will fall short of that needed to fuel adequate growth, the company could be undervalued at the moment (financial institutions tend to have one eye on the future). As the company's value is less than its assets, it could become vulnerable to a takeover.

Against this background, mergers and acquisitions allow companies to add to their pipeline and meet the stock market's expectations for growth. This protects the company from the risk of takeover. Indeed, the stock market's expectation of future share value was a key driver behind the spate of mega-mergers and acquisitions in recent years. Mergers also strengthen the company's financial muscle, making it less vulnerable to takeover and better able to raise capital on the stock market. This capital is invested to enhance the business's productivity. So, share capital might be invested to improve the productivity of R&D or manufacturing. This increases the rate of return on capital (profit). On the other hand, companies are expected to show a rapid return following a merger, e.g. by reducing the number of areas in which the companies overlap and making economies of scale.

The share price is set using a number of measures. This is not the place to explore these in detail – several books are now available. However, the financial highlights often cite several factors that, taken together, allow the stock market and shareholders to value the company. As share options become increasingly popular and widespread as part of an employee's reimbursement package, it is important to understand these definitions. And, of course, remember that small investors do not generally buy or hold shares for the dividend. Rather, they buy shares as a long-term investment. The box should help you make sense of the financial jargon.

---

### Reading the financial pages: a brief lexicon

- **Assets**: A tangible (such as a building) or intangible (e.g. knowledge) object of value to the company that can usually be turned into cash either directly or indirectly
- **Capital**: The total value of assets less liabilities
- **Dividend yield**: Dividend expressed as a percentage of the share value
- **Dividend**: The proportion of earnings that a company pays its shareholders, usually expressed as earnings per share
- **Earnings per share**: *see* Dividend
- **Equities**: The company's ordinary shares – if the company is liquidated, ordinary shareholders split the assets remaining after paying creditors according the number of shares each holds
- **Equity**: The net value after the company's creditors have been paid off
- **Intangible assets**: Intellectual property – such as patents, copyrights and trademarks
- **Loan capital**: The amount of money provided to the company through loans
- **Operating profit**: The company's profit (or loss) made from its main trade – the operating profit is calculated from operating expenses and trading profit before allowing for extraordinary items
- **Revenue**: *see* sales
- **Sales**: The value of the goods that the company sold
- **Share capital**: The amount of money provided to the company by selling shares
- **Tangible assets**: Land, buildings, plant and machinery, fixtures and fittings, trading stock, etc.
- **Trading profit**: The company's profit before deducting interest, directors' fees, auditors' remuneration, and so on
- **Turnover**: Total sales over a defined time – such as annually or quarterly

---

Shares in biotech and pharmaceutical companies are traded worldwide, depending on where the company is based. However, the main markets are London, New York and, to a lesser extent, Frankfurt and Tokyo. These markets differ in several ways, such as the requirements to begin and continue trading, the rules and regulations governing trade, reporting and settlement, as well as their market structure and trading mechanisms. As a result, the markets also differ in their suitability for a particular company.

For example, the London and Wall Street stock market are traditionally conservative, preferring to invest in 'blue-chip' companies, with a well-known name, a good growth record and large assets, rather than a small startup company that has never turned a profit and has few assets other than an innovative idea. This often makes it difficult for small startup companies with an innovative and often untested idea to raise capital on either the London or New York stock market.

In response, the Nasdaq (National Association of Securities Dealers automated quotations) stock market was formed in 1971. The first electronic stock market, the Nasdaq provides an environment that enables small companies to raise capital to commercialise innovative ideas. As a result, many computer and biotech companies, as well as dotcoms, are listed and traded on the Nasdaq. However, as it lacks the stability offered by the blue-chip foundation of traditional markets, prices can vary more widely and it is especially important to take a long-term view. Nevertheless, the Nasdaq continues to help thousands of companies to raise sufficient capital to grow and enter public ownershi-

Traders and shareholders track the market's performance by using several stock market indicators. For example, the Dow Jones Industrial Average, founded in 1884, is an index covering the New York Stock Exchange, based on the performance of 30 companies. While the Industrial Average is the best known of the US indicators, other Dow Jones measures cover movements in US bonds, transportation and utilities. The Nikkei Dow Index indicates the movement of Japanese blue chip shares traded on the Tokyo Stock Exchange.

On the other side of the Atlantic, the *Financial Times* stock exchange 100 index (FTSE100 index or 'Footsie') is based on 100 companies and offers an overall indication of the movement of the London stock market. Again, there are several *Financial Times* share indexes, such as the 54 *Financial Times* actuaries share indexes, which cover various sectors and industries such as capital goods, consumer goods and pharmaceuticals. While less widely quoted, they are influential for investors and portfolio managers. The *Financial Times* ordinary share index is based on 30 market leaders.

## Health service factors

If the problems posed by globalisation and stock market pressures were not enough, there is considerable pressure on prices from the 'customer' – which as we have already noted tends to be the doctor rather than the patient. Indeed, this means the pharmaceutical industry operates within an almost unique marketing dynamic. Unlike most other sectors, the person who chooses and buys the product is *not* the same as the ultimate consumer. It is rather like asking a complete stranger to choose your food on your behalf. Furthermore, governments intervene heavily in most markets to drive down costs. This can lead to a paradox: in countries such as the UK the government wants to encourage the sector's profitability because of the contribution drug companies make to the economy. Meanwhile, another department of the same government wants to keep prices low. The UK experience, which we will look at below, suggests that there might be a solution to this paradox.

## The structure of healthcare systems

However, we will begin by looking at the structure of healthcare systems. While they differ in their details, most healthcare systems tend to be hierarchies. Policy markers, who are either politicians or politically appointed, are at the pinnacle, followed – moving 'down' the hierarchy – by the payers, such as tax-based funds (as in the UK) or statutory social insurance funds (as in Germany and France). The payer pays the purchasers – health maintenance organisations (HMOs) and managed care organisations in the US or primary care organisations in the UK. Next come the provider organisations (hospital, hospices and group primary care practices) and then the prescribers (Johnson, 1995). Patients make up the foundation of the entire system and there is a numerical increase at each layer (Figure 3.1).

---

### Figure 3.1: Hierarchical healthcare

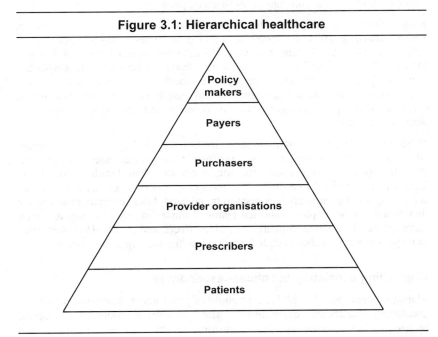

---

However, this is not to play down the importance of local structural differences and the impact that they may have on the marketing strategy for each country. In Sweden, retail pharmacies have been owned and operated by a single state company since 1971 (Ljungkvist *et al.*, 1997). Clearly, this limits opportunities in the OTC market. Moreover, different methods of funding healthcare can be influential. For example, global funds – such as those used in France, Italy, and Canada – help to keep prices down. However, the system leads to inefficiency, such as empty beds. *Per diem* payments, based on the number of days patients are in contact with the healthcare system, are used in Germany and Switzerland and encourage long convalescences, while fee-for-service, payments, such as those in Japan, encourage profligate use of resources (Johnson, 1995).

However, making structural changes to taxation is a nettle few governments are keen to grasp. On the other hand, the amount spent on pharmaceuticals represents an easily identifiable factor in the general heath care expenditure – which is probably why governments tend to focus on drug costs.

The 'soft target' offered by drug expenditure also encourages the increasing trend towards risk sharing in many countries. The system is best developed in the health maintenance organisations (HMOs) in the US, which decide which procedures and drugs they are willing to pay for. As a result, a number of pharmaceutical companies have developed managed care solutions in which they offer more than a drug. They may also offer, for example, a nurse to help with administration, diagnostic services and so on. In some cases, the company agrees to a risk-sharing agreement under which it 'guarantees' a certain outcome – a proportion of cured patients, for example. If it fails, the company faces financial penalties.

Some companies are now developing subsidiaries to work with such organisations. In 1994, for example, Johnson & Johnson formed Johnson & Johnson Health Care Systems Inc., which includes the former Johnson & Johnson Hospital Services and Johnson & Johnson Advanced Behavioral Technologies. Johnson & Johnson Health Care Systems handles contracting and account management with managed care organisations, health maintenance organisations, large hospitals, physician networks, government and employers (Johnson & Johnson website).

While managed care is most advanced in the US, the trend is growing worldwide. Many Asian countries are also expressing interest in managed care , in some cases provided by large corporations for employees and their families (Shahi and Cunningham, 1999). Moreover, as the number of biopharmaceuticals grows, an increasing number of medicines need to be injected. Many companies in Europe and America now employ dedicated teams of nurses to teach patients and their carers about biopharmaceuticals' use, side-effects and so on. However, such managed care approaches need to be tailored to the local medical market.

## Controlling escalating healthcare expenditure

Managed care dovetails with the aspirations of governments worldwide to control escalating healthcare expenditure. Most countries attempt to control pharmaceutical expenditure and consumption by influencing prices and reimbursement – with varying degrees of success. In most EU counties, government-appointed committees decide whether to approve a company's proposed price for a new pharmaceutical based on a dossier of cost and benefits as well as domestic and international price comparisons. In contrast, the UK's system leaves the company free to price products at a level defined by the market. This is something few other systems – other than the unfettered free market in the US – manage. Table 3.1 shows the main cost containment methods used in Europe.

Indeed, the UK's pharmaceutical price regulation scheme (PPRS; see box) balances competing economic imperatives. The PPRS limited increases in UK pharmaceutical prices to an average of less than 0.5% annually since 1993. Indeed, the ABPI estimated that a basket of the top 10 community prescription products dropped in price by 41% between 1988 and 1998. The PPRS allows producers considerable discretion to set prices for new drugs without government

## Table 3.1: Main cost containment methods used in Europe

| | A | B | DK | FIN | F | D | GR | IC | IRL | I | L | NL | N | P | E | S | CH | GB |
|---|---|---|---|---|---|---|---|---|---|---|---|---|---|---|---|---|---|---|
| Control of ex-manufacturer price | x | o | x | o | x | x | o | o | x | x | o | x | o | o | o | x | x | x |
| Control of reimbursement entry | o | o | o | o | o | x | o | x | x | o | o | o | o | o | o | o | o | x |
| Cross-country comparison | o | o | o | o | o | x | o | o | o | o | o | o | o | o | o | o | o | x |
| Reference pricing | x | x | o | x | x | o | x | o | x | x | x | o | o | x | (x) | o | x | x |
| Payback/contracts | o | x | x | x | o | x | x | x | o | o | x | x | x | (x) | (o) | o | x | o |
| Profit control | x | x | x | x | x | x | x | x | x | x | x | x | x | x | o | x | x | o |
| Promotional spend control | x | (x) | x | x | o | x | x | x | x | x | x | x | x | x | o | x | x | o |
| Prescribing budgets | x | x | x | x | x | o | x | x | o | x | x | x | x | x | o | x | x | o |
| Pharmaco-economic evidence recommended | x | x | x | o | x | x | x | x | x | o | x | o | o | o | x | o | x | o |
| Fixed wholesale margin | o | o | x | x | o | o | o | x | o | o | o | o | x | o | x | x | o | o |
| Fixed pharmacy margin | o | o | o | o | o | o | o | o | o | o | o | o | o | o | o | o | o | o |
| Generic substitution | x | x | o | o | o | x | x | x | x | o | o | o | o | x | (x) | x | x | x |
| Patient copayment | o | o | o | o | o | o | o | o | o | o | o | x | o | o | o | o | o | o |
| Control of OTC price | x | o | x | x | x | x | o | x | x | x | o | x | x | x | x | x | x | x |
| Control of hospital price | x | o | x | x | x | x | o | x | x | o | x | x | x | x | o | x | x | x |

A = Austria; B = Belgium; DK = Denmark; FIN = Finland; F = France; D = Germany; GR = Greece; IC = Iceland; IRL = Ireland; I = Italy; L = Luxembourg; NL = Netherlands; N = Norway; OTC = over-the-counter; P = Portugal; E = Spain; S = Sweden; CH = Switzerland; GB = United Kingdom.

o = yes; x = no; (o)/(x) = situation changing.

Source: Donald Macarthur

interference. As a result, prices are somewhat higher than in comparable European countries. On the other hand, UK utilisation rates are among the lowest, reflecting British doctors' conservative nature. Burstall (1997) concludes that the PPRS curbed spending on pharmaceuticals 'with minimal damage' to the pharmaceutical sector.

---

### The pharmaceutical price regulation scheme

The pharmaceutical price regulation scheme (PPRS) is a voluntary 5-year agreement between the government and the ABPI, the UK's industry body. The PPRS restricts each company's profits on the combined sales of its branded medicines (it does not apply to generics) by setting a target return on capital. (Companies without major capital UK investments work on return on sales.) The agreement allows for certain expenses, such as research, marketing and administration. The PPRS does not guarantee profits, imposes tight restrictions on price increases and applies only if the company makes a profit.

The PPRS has three main aims:

*   To secure a supply of safe, effective, reasonably priced medicines

*   To promote a strong, profitable pharmaceutical industry capable of the sustained R&D expenditure needed to develop new and improved medicines

*   To encourage the efficient, competitive development and supply of medicines to worldwide pharmaceutical markets.

To achieve these three aims, the PPRS caps the return on capital, after allowances, to an average of between 17% and 18%, although the maximum is 21%. This keeps profit on NHS sales in line with the average profitability of leading companies in other sectors. The PPRS also restricts spending on sales promotion to between 7% and 8% of NHS income.

If the company exceeds its target, it can keep only up to 40% above the original permitted return. Anything over this must be repaid either by cutting prices, repaying the excess profit to the government or either delaying or restricting previously agreed price rises.

---

## Pharmaco-economics and the fourth hurdle

Potentially one of the biggest changes to the healthcare market is the emergence of pharmaco-economics as the fourth implicit or explicit regulatory hurdle (the other three being safety, efficacy and quality). Australia was the first country to introduce a mandatory requirement for economic evaluation in 1993. Canada followed in 1994 (Hess *et al.*, 1999). Economic evaluation is now part of the package for pricing and reimbursement for at least some products in the Netherlands, Portugal and Finland. In the US, many health maintenance organisations and other healthcare providers require such information before agreeing to fund an agent. And the UK established the National Institute for Clinical Excellence (NICE) in 1999 to recommend, on the basis of cost and clinical effectiveness, whether a drug should be prescribed on the National Health Service (NHS; Backhouse and Mauskopf, 2000).

As a result, most large companies now have an in-house health economics department that conducts studies throughout the product life cycle. However, there is also a growing demand for outsourced health economics consultancy from both academia and the private sector. This s produced a marked increase in the number of health economic publications: 541 were published between 1995 and 1997 (Backhouse and Mauskopf, 2000). This trend shows no signs of slowing down.

Many countries are considering whether to implement a formal health technology assessment organisation similar to NICE. In the meantime, however, the Canadian, Dutch or Australian 'fourth hurdles' are little more than nuisances in the context of global development. In contrast, NICE is of strategic significance for pharmaceutical companies worldwide, for three main reasons (Greener, 2000b). First, NICE is the first such health technology assessment authority in a traditional major pharmaceutical market. Second, NICE critically appraises the clinical *and* economic evidence rather than just one or the other. Finally, preparing for the NICE appraisal needs to begin early in the drug's clinical development, which influences the development of clinical trials and the evidence needed. Against this background, the reasons underlying NICE's assessment – positive and negative – could carry over into other jurisdictions.

## Orphan drugs

Some diseases affect too few people for conventional R&D to be profitable. However, taken together, the more than 5,000 'rare' diseases worldwide affect millions of people, although they can be widely scattered throughout the developed and developing world. This means that the markets are relatively small, especially in the developed world. As a result, US, European and Japanese governments aim to encourage research into and the development of drugs for 'orphan' diseases – defined as those affecting less than 0.1% of the population in Europe and the EU and less than 0.04% in Japan. However, orphan disease status applies only if the company will be unable to generate an adequate return to justify the investment (Minghetti *et al.*, 2000a).

Japan led the way, providing financial support for orphan drug development in 1973. The government offers R&D grants, tax reductions, guidance to speed the development and so on (Minghetti *et al.*, 2000a). The US followed, introducing specific orphan drug legislation in 1983. Over the next 12 years, 631 applications for orphan status were accepted for 450 drugs. Of these, the FDA granted 121 marketing approvals. The US offers grants to support clinical trials, tax credits, 7 years' marketing exclusivity for the orphan indication, fast-track approval, assistance from the regulatory bodies, and so on. Some countries – such as Australia – automatically recognise orphan drugs approved in the US. In October 2000, the European Commission awarded orphan drug status to eight medicines, including treatments for AIDS-related muscle loss, some cancers and metabolic diseases. The manufacturers obtain accelerated approval, a 10-year monopoly and tax breaks.

Recognising the need to develop medicines for 'unprofitable' conditions – such as the orphan drug programme – illustrates a key feature of the pharmaceutical industry: it does not operate in a truly free market. The sector needs to work with governments, healthcare agencies and patients to meet unmet healthcare needs. Its methods of research raise ethical and moral dilemmas. But, unlike the arms trade, which also need to operate within tight regulation and consider the ethical dimension, pharmaceuticals regularly and directly affects us all. This combination of circumstances sets pharmaceuticals apart from other industry sectors.

## Patient advocacy

The days when patients were silent recipients of healthcare are long gone. Patients increasingly demand an influential voice in their healthcare and information about the treatments they receive. As a result, there has been a dramatic increase in the number of patient groups as well as in their influence on governments and the pharmaceutical sector. Currently, the US leads the way with between 750,000 and 1,000,000 patient groups. This reflects, in part, the fact that American patients fund their healthcare either directly or indirectly through employers' health insurance. It also reflects the US's litigious culture, which encourages advocacy. Nevertheless, Germany, the UK and Denmark have around 70,000, 50,000 and 1,200 patient groups respectively.

Recently, patient groups have organised themselves into effective lobbies with considerable reach (Figure 3.2). Most patient groups tend to be geographical – the UK's National Osteoporosis Society, the US-based National Osteoporosis Foundation and Foundation for Osteoporosis Research and Education, for example. However, patient groups also organise into transnational organisations – such as the International Osteoporosis Foundation. Currently, however, the global view tends to take second place to national interests.

### Figure 3.2: The reach of patient power

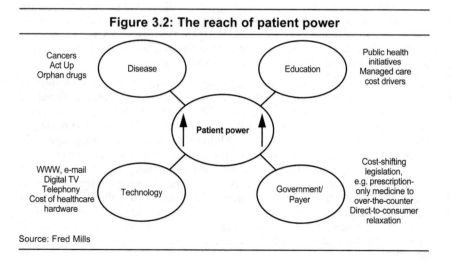

Source: Fred Mills

Nevertheless, the Internet encourages transnational communication between patients. Apart from easy access to sites, some providers such as the Yahoo! Dr Kroop group offer vitual patient communities. In particular, these are reaching eastern Europe and China, where patient advocacy is still in its infancy. Moreover, the Internet allows patients to access a wealth of information that helps inform their decision and is beginning – augmented by the growing amount of health information available in mainstream media – to fundamentally change patients' relationships with their doctors. As we will see, the growing numbers of vocal, informed patients is also beginning to alter pharmaceutical companies' marketing strategies.

On the other hand, the success of some vocal patient advocacy groups means that many smaller groups struggle to be heard. As a result, patient groups are increasingly consolidating under umbrella groups. For example, Eurodis, the European Organisation for Rare Diseases, includes 85 local and national organisations in 12 countries covering over 2,000 rare diseases. Health Action International is a global network of organisations in over 70 countries representing consumers' interests in drug policy. However, there is a danger that the voices and interests of smaller groups could be diluted as part of a larger organisation.

Nevertheless, the growing importance of advocacy organisations means that pharmaceutical companies increasingly work with patient groups. As a result, the increasing influence of such groups is changing the market dynamics and drug companies' marketing strategies.

Traditionally, pharmaceutical companies relied on an indirect route to reach patients. According to this model (Figure 3.3), persuading healthcare professionals – doctors, pharmacists and nurses – of a drug's merit will ensure that the treatment is adopted. Patients had little influence. This method assumed that healthcare professionals passed information on to the consumer. However, the message inevitably became diluted through the various layers.

## Figure 3.3: Sources of patient information

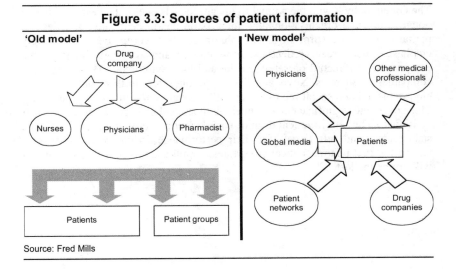

Source: Fred Mills

Under the new model, physicians, global media – such as the Internet – patient networks, other health professionals and drug companies compete for the patients' attention. All these offer patients information and, in some cases, the advice could conflict. The pharmaceutical company needs to embrace and influence these media to reach as many people as possible. However, this also changes the dynamic between patients and their doctors. For example, direct-to-consumer advertising appeals directly to the patient, bypassing the clinician. As we will see in Chapter 7, this raises concerns about whether this is a 'legitimate' promotional route.

## The influence of nongovernmental organisations

Patient advocacy is one example of a broader trend in society: the growing influence exerted by nongovernmental organisations (NGOs). These groups are, partly, a response to the globalisation embraced by the pharmaceutical sector and industry more generally. These lobby groups use new technology to break into the formerly hidden world of local governments, country government, the EU and even wider in international relations (Taylor, 2000).

As a result, pharmaceutical companies – indeed any corporation, in any business field – increasingly integrate corporate affairs into their marketing mix and try to build alliances with nongovernmental groups. Monsanto's experience offers a sobering reminder of what can happen if companies fail to take account of these new groups. The emergence of a virulent European anti-genetic-modification lobby weakened Monsanto. This lobby crystallised around an EU directive that fixed the conditions under which genetically modified organisms could be introduced. While Monsanto is not the only company working on genetically modified organisms, it had the highest profile and bore the brunt of the activists' anger. Monsanto's troubles threatened its stock-market status and contributed to its recent acquisition by Pharmacia & Upjohn.

The Green lobby – with the animal rights groups – is one of the best-established nongovernmental organisations that impacts on pharmaceutical companies. So perhaps it is not surprising that pharmaceutical companies increasingly emphasise their green credentials. Most current annual reports highlight the company's track record on safety, health and the environment. However, some companies – such as Novo Nordisk – go one step further, publishing an environmental and social report along with their more traditional annual report. This covers the 'significant environmental, bioethical and social aspects' of their activities. The environmental and social report aims to engage all the stakeholders and sets targets for their performance. While Novo Nordisk is among the first pharmaceutical companies to embrace this new market ethic, it will not be the last.

# Chapter 4: Drug discovery

In most sectors of today's 'affluent society', advertising and salesmanship create desires – wants that did not previously exist. The company's goods meet these created desires (Galbraith, 1997, p. 129). So advertising-driven desires for a new car, a new washing machine or a new soft drink are artificial. We do not need them to survive and thrive. This is not the case in medicine. The unmet needs are real, rather than artificially created, and are waiting in every doctor's surgery.

## What is illness?

Obviously, medical science and the pharmaceutical industry treat illness. However, it is worth taking a step back and considering what we mean by illness. We will return to this theme in Chapter 10, during a consideration of whether obesity is a disease. In this chapter, however, we will stick to less controversial illnesses. But even here, defining illness is somewhat arbitrary. Blood pressure and lipid levels, for example, have a normal 'bell-shaped' or 'n-shaped' distribution. In such cases, the abnormality is quantitative rather than qualitative. As a result, the point at which clinicians decide that something is abnormal, and therefore warrants treatment, is an arbitrary decision usually based on population risk (Rose, 1993. pp. 6–8). This means that different clinicians can – and sometimes do – draw different conclusions about the point at which they will intervene. Clearly, such factors can influence the success of a particular medication.

This point was first made by George Pickering in his considerations of hypertension in the early 1950s – and provoked a furious debate. Now it is clear that even infections may range from severe clinical infection to asymptomatic colonisation, while cancer ranges from premalignant cellular changes to massively invasive tumours (Rose, 1993, pp. 6–8). Severe infections and massively invasive tumours should be obvious even to a clinical tyro; asymptomatic colonisation and premalignant cellular changes are often only evident using sophisticated laboratory equipment. As diagnostic technology develops, researchers are able to detect ever more subtle changes, which alters our understanding of 'normality'.

These are more than academic arguments. As mentioned above, they can influence the intervention threshold and, therefore, the pharmaceutical market. However, they also strike at the heart of a deeper debate facing society. For example, life itself may be considered to be a continuum from the potential in an unfertilised egg or swimming sperm to the birth of a child (Rose, 1993, pp. 6–8). The former is, in some ways, akin to the potential of premalignant cellular changes to evolve into a cancer. The point at which life begins is, therefore, difficult to define. Is it in the potential of the egg and sperm? The point of fertilisation? The point at which the child is capable of independent existence? (See Connee, 1999 and Singer's *Practical Ethics* (1993) for a further discussion of these philosophical positions supporting these points.)

Such arguments influence companies making contraceptives and, in particular, abortifacients and morning-after pills. But the arguments also influence biotech companies and researchers wanting to use fetal tissue therapeutically. These positions help set the market and the sociological conditions within which the pharmaceutical sector works. And the arguments underline, once again, that biomedical research cannot exist in a ethical vacuum.

## Unmet clinical needs

Fortunately, such ethical dilemmas are relatively uncommon. Most major areas of unmet clinical need are in ethically less tricky areas. Indeed, just seven conditions still account for around half the total loss of life among people less than 65 years of age in the UK (Rose, 1993, p. 98):

- Coronary heart disease
- Road traffic accidents
- Pneumonia and bronchitis
- Lung cancer
- Breast cancer
- Suicide
- Stroke.

Pharmaceuticals could either directly or indirectly affect all of these. The role of pharmaceuticals in combating coronary heart disease, cancers and lung infection is self-evident. However, pharmaceuticals also help to counter some wider public health issues. Less sedative hypnotics and antihistamines, as well as drugs to counter chronic alcoholism, could help to reduce some of the factors contributing to road traffic accidents. Similarly, better-tolerated and more effective psychiatric agents could help to reduce the number of people who take their own lives.

However, if health services better implemented the evidence base available today, clinicians would probably half premature mortality from these causes (Rose, 1993, p. 98). This underlies the considerable problems facing the industry and health services when attempting to promote better healthcare. But even here the pharmaceutical sector may be able help to drive improved outcomes through managed care initiatives and by ensuring that the evidence base supporting a drug is relevant and can be implemented.

## The aims of drug discovery

Against this background, drug discovery has three main aims:

- Treating previously untreatable diseases
- Increasing the effectiveness of treatments for diseases for which there are already medicines available
- Reducing the incidence or severity of side-effects.

To meet these aims, drug discovery scientists:

- Identify a target
- Identify that a chemical that alters the target's biological function
- Characterise the drug and its safety in animals.

And it is the last point that causes the most consternation among the general public.

## Identifying a lead compound

Traditionally, pharmacology advanced in fits and starts. At its simplest, chemists would either isolate a chemical from a plant or synthesise it in the lab. The former was the commonest way to identify a drug. Research scientists often used to bring samples of soil and flora home from their annual vacation to test for possible new drugs. Indeed, until the 1950s, most drugs derived from vascular plants. Flowering plants and ferns led to 120 commercial drugs, which account for a quarter of US prescriptions.

And many plant-derived products are household names – e.g. aspirin, theophylline and quinine. Moreover, in 1992, the FDA approved taxol, from the Pacific yew tree (*Taxus brevifolia*), for ovarian cancer and 2 years later for metastatic breast cancer. Taxol, today one of the world's largest selling drugs (Table 2.17), emerged from a screening programme instigated by the US National Cancer Institute in the 1960s (Cox and Balick, 1994).

Despite its success, by the mid 1980s, most drug companies had abandoned using vascular plants as a source of new medicines. Many came to regret their decision. Indeed, since the late 1990s, many companies have realised the potential offered by the study of indigenous herbal medicine – a discipline called ethanobotany (Cox and Balick, 1994). As discussed in Chapter 10, there has recently been a resurgence of interest in ethanobotany as researchers look for chemical leads for the thousands of targets yielded by the genomics revolution.

In other cases, researchers may search the literature or the company's chemical database for chemicals that have a similar action but that proved ineffective or had too many side-effects. Chemists can, by modifying the structure, lead to more active or less toxic variations. As discussed Chapter 1, this is broadly the approach that was used to make heroin and aspirin.

More recently, researchers have begun with the disease that they wanted to treat. As molecular biology progressed, scientists began to unravel the complex biochemical pathways that cause an effect, such as increasing blood pressure. They knew the enzymes and receptors responsible and, in many cases, their 3D structure. Through a combination of computer modelling and chemical modification, researchers were able to develop specific drugs that bound to the enzyme or receptor. This targeted approach increases the likelihood that the researchers will develop an agent with the desired therapeutic effect.

Pharmacologists would test promising chemicals on well-established tests. For example, they might record the effects on a piece of tissue, such as a section of a guinea pig's intestine, add a variety of drugs that blocked the different receptors and discover the chemical's characteristics. After testing on a variety of tissues, the pharmacologist would offer some insight into the type of diseases it might treat. This hypothesis could then be tested in live animal experiments.

More recently, cell culture added another experimental method. In cell culture, cells are grow in a sheet on flat-bottomed bottles bathed in a solution that keeps the culture alive. The researcher can add a drug and see what happens to the cells. For example, if the cells die, that might indicate toxicity. More sophisticated experiments look at the cells' production of certain biological chemicals, such as cytokines (proteins that carry messages between cells). So, for instance, if a drug reduces production of an inflammatory cytokines it may be useful in inflammatory diseases, such as asthma or eczema.

Moreover, cell culture experiments allow researchers to examine the effect of drugs on signalling pathways within cells. For example, cancer cells grown in culture often show disrupted pathways and altered production of key cytokines. Drugs that modulate these pathways or normalise production of the cytokines may be possible treatments for cancer. However, this can be confirmed only by experimental studies in animals and humans. Indeed, while cell culture and isolated organ experiments can offer insights into what happens to a cell or organ, they cannot inform scientists about the drug's effects on a whole organism. To answer these questions animal experiments are necessary.

## Testing and safety

Animal research bridges the gap between the test tube and the clinical trial programme described in the next chapter. While there are obvious differences between animals and humans, basic mammalian physiology is broadly similar in a rat and a human. This means that animal testing offers an important indication of safety and effectiveness of a drug in humans.

Animal experimentation is nothing new. Greek and Roman physicians learnt much of their anatomy from dissecting animals. Animal experimentation even has a long history of use in assessing the effectiveness of new drugs. In 1650, Christopher Wren and Robert Boyle used opium to demonstrate the new technique of intravenous injection using the pen quill. The injection 'stupefied' dogs and other researchers found that the animals would not respond to their commands (Miller and Tran, 2000).

Researchers perform experiments in animals firstly to establish efficacy. In some cases, a normal healthy animal is an acceptable model for the condition. (However, animals used in experiments are, as far as possible, genetically similar. This reduces the number of factors that might influence the results.) For example, the mechanisms controlling the pressure inside the eye (intra-ocular pressure) are similar in rabbits and humans. As a result, rabbits can be used to assess the effectiveness of drugs that lower pressure in the eye. Such treatments are needed to prevent the progression of glaucoma, one of the commonest causes of blindness in the developed world. The same principle applies to hypertension, for example.

In a growing number of cases, however, researchers want to study a disease that does not have a direct parallel in animals, at least in a species suitable for experimentation. As a result, they either breed or genetically engineer an animal to express a feature appropriate for study. So you can breed some animals to have develop a particular type of cancer or have markedly elevated blood pressure. The first genetically modified animal was bred in the early 1980s, when the gene for human growth hormone was inserted into a pig (Rollin, 1995, p. 22). Since then many animals have been bred with specific genetic abnormalities. Indeed, knockout mice (where a gene is knocked out to examine the effect) are essential for studies of functional genomics (see below).

---

### A mouse with osteoporosis

Osteoporosis imposes a considerable toll on health services worldwide – and it is a problem set to increase with the ageing population (see Chapter 10). For instance, half of women and one in six men sustain an osteoporosis-related fracture by 90 years of age and mortality increases by 20% in the year following a hip fracture (Peel and Eastell, 1995). However, the lack of an animal model hampered the study of new treatments. To counter this, researchers developed a transgenic mouse that inappropriately expresses the cytokine interleukin 4 (IL-4). This reduces bone formation by cells called osteoblasts, as happens in many case of osteoporosis (Lewis *et al.*, 1993). The model allows researchers to asses the effect of drugs that increase bone mass by altering the activity of osteoblasts.

---

In general, any potential drug is tested on one or two species – usually rodents – to see whether it exerts any effect. If the drug proves promising, it may be tested on a wider range of animals, including cats, dogs, pigs and a number of other species. The researchers choose the animal tests to ensure that the work offers the best insight into what might happen in humans.

In the meantime, the drug needs to be assessed for safety, pharmacokinetics and pharmacodynamics. Pharmacokinetic studies aim to characterise how the body handles a drug. So a pharmacokinetic study characterises the drug's absorption, distribution, metabolism and excretion (ADME). This may involve injecting the animal with a radiolabelled drug and measuring radioactivity levels in the urine, faeces and tissues. In contrast, pharmacodynamic studies characterise the drug's biological effects. So pharmacodynamic studies may explore how the drug interacts with cells – its effects, adverse reactions, dose-response, etc.

To assess safety, animals, again usually rodents, are fed or injected with large quantities of a drug and then humanely killed. Samples of the tissue are taken and any changes are noted. The organs are also carefully examined under the microscope. Moreover, the effect on behaviour might also be assessed, using a number of tests. Animals may also be dosed with increasing quantities of the drug until the dose kills half the treated animals (the so-called $LD_{50}$). In other experiments, animals are dosed with the drug for several months to see if chronic side-effects, such as cancer, emerge. Finally, the animal toxicological screen assesses reproductive toxicology even if a drug is not to be used during pregnancy. A UK survey revealed that 35% of women had taken medicines at least once during pregnancy. Moreover, 6% had taken medicines other than iron and vitamin supplements during the critical first 3 months (Barnes, 2000).

Overall, most experiments are performed in rodents, which account for some 85% of the total animals used in biological R&D. Dogs and cats account for 0.4%, with a variety of other species making up the difference. On the basis of this assessment, which uses doses higher than those that will be employed clinically to offer a safety margin, the company can apply to test the drug in human volunteers (see Chapter 5.)

## The ethics of using animals in research

The ethical issues surrounding the use of animals in research is one of the most difficult areas for the pharmaceutical industry. There are two points worth making before boldly treading into this minefield. First, there is increasing evidence that some nonhuman primates may be self-aware. So, chimpanzees, orang-utans and gorillas are specifically excluded from the following debate. They are rarely used in pharmaceutical research in any case. Second, the debate excludes the testing of cosmetics, skin care products, food additives, shampoos and so on. These tests are not necessary to reduce human suffering. As Peter Singer notes (1993, pp, 65–66) we already have enough shampoos and food colorants. The ethical debate below concerns only the use of animals to alleviate human suffering arising from disease, either through treatment or prevention. The distinction is crucial.

It is also worth mentioning that everyone, including researchers, would welcome a reduction in the number of animals used in scientific experiments. Indeed, advances in biological knowledge and new technology (see below) mean that the number of animals used in many areas of research has halved over the last 20 years. Moreover, research worldwide is controlled by strict legislation: in most countries, the researchers and the premises need to be licensed and veterinary care must be available, for example. Indeed, the first law governing animal experiments was passed in Britain as long ago as 1876 (Rollin, 1995, p. 148). Most developed countries either implemented new legislation or radically revised their laws in the 1980s in the light of growing public concern.

The legislation, as well as researchers' own ethical standards, mean that pharmaceutical companies design experiments to use the minimum number of animals and employ alternatives whenever possible. Moreover, increasing harmonisation between regulatory authorities worldwide (see Chapter 8) means that requirements for animal tests are increasingly consistent. This avoids duplicating animal work. Despite this, the number of animals used in medical research is growing. Medical science is expanding rapidly. As a result, research into new areas, safety concerns and public health issues means that the number of animals is increasing. Inevitably, some animals suffer pain and discomfort as a result.

There are essentially two positions surrounding the discomfort of animals in scientific experiments. First, the utilitarian. After giving equal consideration to the position of animals, the utilitarian argument holds that allowing controlled animal experimentation brings a greater sum of reduction in suffering than not experimenting (Singer, 1993, p. 67). Few people would disagree that humans suffer more than animals from the same degree of discomfort, largely because of humans' self-awareness. So, a human in pain from cancer suffers more than a rodent in pain from a similar tumour, because the patient has greater awareness. In this way, you cannot equate the suffering between rats and people: the human suffers more. But as Singer (1993, pp. 58–59) notes, while the utilitarian argument may justify using animals in experiments to reduce human suffering, it does not abrogate humans from considering the animals' interests and, as far as possible, minimising their discomfort.

The other view is absolute. This holds that it is wrong to sacrifice one being – human or animal – to benefit another. As a result, all animal experimentation is wrong (Singer, 1993, p. 67). It is often forgotten by researchers in the drug industry that such positions are justified from well-considered, internally logical, ethical, philosophical and religious values and beliefs. Whether you adhere to the utilitarian or absolute ethic is a value judgement. Researchers will not be able to enter an informed debate without appreciating the other view – and, of course, the converse is equally true.

Moreover, the use of genetically modified (transgenic) animals raises other ethical and practical concerns. Would it be ethically correct to genetically modify an animal so that it does not feel pain or discomfort when experimented on? Would this give researchers carte blanche for any experiment? Is it right to engineer an animal knowing that this condemns it to a life of discomfort? What if a genetically engineered mouse escaped (or was liberated) and bred with the local population?

---

### A thought experiment

Image an animal in a sealed cage connected to cyanide gas that would painlessly kill the animal. You can simply push a button and the animal dies quickly. If killing one mouse would save thousands of humans dying of AIDS, would that be justified? If killing one mouse would save your father from dying of cancer, would that be justified? If killing 1,000 mice would save one human life, would that be justified? What if it was a dog instead of a mouse? Or a Rhesus monkey?

These are of course facile arguments – experiments do not produce such dramatic and easily identifiable outcomes. But they may help to clarify your thoughts about the competing respective rights of animals and humans. There are no right answers. It is a question of values.

---

This is a huge ethical area and anyone who works for the sector needs to be aware of the issues. I have only scratched the surface here – Bernard Rollin's and Peter Singer's books are essential reading for any one interested in the debate (and that should be anyone working in any sector in the industry).

For what it's worth, I think I should lay my ethical cards on the table. The competing rights of humans for freedom from disease and animals for welfare can and should be balanced. But I believe that animal research is essential to reduce the sum of human suffering. Until alternatives become available, animal research is inevitable and justified. However, that does not offer anyone carte blanche to exploit animals as a short cut to profit. Animals have rights. As a society, we need to respect those rights, remain aware of those rights at all times and ensure that animal welfare is not compromised to a greater degree than is unavoidable in the search for new drugs.

## New developments

Despite all the research and the remarkable strides basic science has made, we have barely scratched the surface of human biology. For example, scientists may have characterised less than a third of the neurotransmitters, neuromodulators, growth factors, growth inhibitory factors, and so on that play crucial roles in brain development and function (Young and Palmour, 1999). This underlines the importance of basic research. Scientists need to appreciate the role played by these biochemical instruments in the symphony of life. That means investing money in research that may, at first sight, seem obscure. For example, studies using larval zebrafish can visualise neural firing patterns and the fruit fly *Drosophila melanogaster* offers insights into the molecular and genetic control of behaviour (Hendricks *et al.*, 2000). Such experiments generate hypotheses that researchers can test in other animals.

So, despite the undoubted success of the modern pharmaceutical industry, plenty more drugs remain to be discovered. Estimates of the number of possible drug molecules are some $10^{40}$ (10 followed by 40 0s). Most companies have access to only 500,000–1,000,000 molecules. Clearly, companies need some way to increase their chances of success (Valler and Green, 2000). The details of these techniques are outside the scope of this book (but see Valler and Green, 2000 for more details). However, they all aim to increase companies' chances of success.

Indeed, many companies now place their faith in technology – computer-aided drug design, combinational chemistry, high-throughput screening and so on – to overcome the innovation deficit. High-throughput screening alone increases the number of assays for new drugs from 10,000 a year to 100,000 – or even more – every day. Indeed, screening 100,000 samples per day in miniaturised assay volumes will soon become routine. Today, most pharmaceutical companies use high-throughput screening as the primary engine driving lead discovery (Hertzberg and Pope, 2000). But these high-tech approaches have yet to have much impact on the market place. In 1999, for example, the top 20 companies admitted than none had marketed a new product based on a lead derived from combinational chemistry and high-throughput screening (Horrobin, 2000).

## The Human Genome Project

However, the Human Genome Project is likely to have the largest impact on drug discovery. As you probably know, the Human Genome Project, along with genomic studies of other organisms, aims to characterise the genetic code. From this, researchers hope that they will gain a better understanding of biology generally and generate numerous new targets for drugs and other interventions.

The Human Genome Project rests on the so-called 'central dogma' of molecular biology. In 1958, Francis Crick, who with James Watson described the structure of DNA in 1953, developed the central dogma of molecular biology. Stated simply, this holds that information flows from DNA to RNA (transcription) to protein (translation). In general, information flows one way. However, a group of viruses, including human immunodeficiency virus (HIV) and some cancer viruses, store information as RNA rather than DNA. As a result, the code needs to be transcribed first into DNA. This is performed by a group of enzymes called reverse transcriptases, discovered in 1970 (Kanehisa, 2000, pp. 6–7). Many drugs used to treat HIV and acquired immune deficiency syndrome (AIDS) inhibit HIV reverse transcriptase.

You may remember that DNA and RNA consist of chains of nucleotides – in DNA adenine, guanine, cytosine and thymine; in RNA adenine, guanine, cytosine and uracil. The complexities of how the genotype (what is inherited) leads to the phenotype (what this produces) is outside the scope of this book. But in essence, mixes of these nucleotides code for amino acids, the building blocks of protein. So three uracils codes for phenylalanine, uracil–adenine–uracil for tyrosine, cytosine–cytosine–uracil for proline, and so on.

The 20 amino acids join together to form proteins. After modification by enzymes, (post-transcriptional modification) these proteins can form enzymes, receptors and so on. Knowing the sequence of amino acids in a protein offers some insight into its structure. Each amino acids has a different structure. This means that it brings different physical properties to the protein. So, a particular amino acid may have an affinity for water (hydrophilic) or be repelled by water (hydrophobic). This allows researchers to determine the proteins structure – for example, by making a crystal of the protein and looking at the way it influences the passage of X-rays. Based on these factors, chemists can design drugs that bind to these proteins.

So to summarise: The central dogma suggests that if we know the genetic sequence we should also know the amino acid product. This should allow us to know the proteins' shape and physical properties. This is a critical piece in the jigsaw that allows researchers to develop a targeted therapy. It sounds simple. But the scale of the Human Genome Project is daunting.

Firstly, the genome contains an incredible amount of information. Viruses contain between $10^3$ and $10^5$ (1,000–100,000) nucleotides. Free-living organisms (viruses act as parasites in other cells) contain between $10^6$ and $10^9$ nucleotides. So, bacteria contain around 1 million nucleotides. The human genome contains 3 billion nucleotides and 100,000 genes (Kanehisa, 2000, pp. 14–15).

Secondly, once you have the gene sequence, you need to discover what it codes for. Knowing a gene's sequence and even the protein structure tells us relatively little about the encoded protein's function. And discovering that is not an easy task. Scientists isolated the BRCA1 gene, associated with familial breast cancer, in 1994. Despite 6 years of intensive research, the role of BRCA1 in normal and transformed cells remains unclear (Richmond, 1999).

You can gain an impression of the scale of the problem by considering one chromosome, number 22, which may contain up to 1,000 genes. Only 545 of the putative genes encode either known proteins or homologues (Little, 1999). Moreover, single genes cause very few diseases. Most diseases are multifactorial. So researchers need to understand the function of several genes and how they interact. Lesch–Nyhan syndrome (see box) offers another sobering reminder of our lack of understanding of some basic biological pathways.

## The mystery of Lesch–Nyhan syndrome

Lesch–Nyhan syndrome is a rare, X-linked, recessive metabolic disorder. Children develop a number of symptoms, including biochemical disturbances, dystonia (muscle weakness) and aggressive behaviour. They may also injure themselves.

Scientists know that Lesch–Nyhan syndrome is caused by a deficiency of the enzyme hypoxanthine phosphoribosyltransferase (HPRT). They know that this deficiency leads to overproduction of purines (a biochemical product) by another pathway. They know that this leads to an increase in uric acid and the symptoms of gout. But as Young and Palmour note 'after 25 years of research, there is still no understanding of how a deficiency in HPRT leads to neuropsychiatric symptoms, let alone to specific and dramatic behavioural symptoms such as self-mutilation'. There are hints, certainly. A low level of dopamine seems to be influential, for example. But 'molecular genetic techniques have not been particularly helpful' in either unravelling the causes of Lesch–Nyhan syndrome or improving therapy (Young and Palmour, 1999).

Thirdly, once you have the amino acid structure and once you know the gene products' role, you need to elucidate the structure of the protein in order to design drugs that act as antagonists or agonists. Again, this leaves companies facing a massive technological issue. IBM is now working on a supercomputer some 500 times more powerful than the largest current supercomputer in order to model protein folding and structure (Horrobin, 2000).

Finally, you have to work out how genes interact with each other and with the environment, as well as how expression changes over the animal's lifetime. Unravelling these complexities can be difficult, to say the least. For example, knockout mice without serotonin 5-HT$_{1b}$ receptors are more aggressive, self-administer cocaine faster and drink more alcohol than controls. (In humans also, decreased 5-HT$_{1b}$ receptor function appears to be linked to antisocial alcoholism.) This suggests that decreased 5-HT$_{1b}$ receptor function is linked to aggression. However, it is not as simple as this. Other knockout mice are also aggressive. So female knockout mice without oestrogen receptors are more aggressive than control females. Males with the same knockout are less aggressive than normal males (Young and Palmour, 1999). Therefore, to explore the biological determinants of aggression, researchers need to characterise the relative importance of these various receptors.

Moreover, genes interact with the environment. And this can prove a key factor. It is genetically determined that we have the capacity to learn language. But whether we speak English, French or Swahili depends on the environment (Maynard Smith, 1993, p. 242). Similarly, in heart disease, expressing high levels of cholesterol is, at least partly, genetically determined. However, if people eat a low fat diet and remain active they may be able to avoid suffering a heart attack.

All this underlines the continuing need for basic biological research. Certainly some fundamental questions remain unanswered. Most researchers believe that human chromosomes code for around 10,000 proteins. Even if this is right by an order of magnitude, there appears to be too much DNA by a factor of at least 100 (Maynard Smith, 1993, p. 125). The biological role of this nongene (intron) DNA is unclear. Moreover, not all genes are expressed all the time. Studies on the *Drosophila* fly, the nematode worm *Caenorhabditis* and the plant *Arabidopsis* have begun to characterise genes concerned with development. The researchers determined the nucleotide sequence, the time and stage in the cycle when they are active and the interactions involved (Maynard Smith, 1993, p. 21). This is beginning to be examined in human genomics.

All this is tremendously exciting for anyone interested in biological research. But it is important to keep the advances in context. As Young and Palmour (1999) comment: 'Research on genes has immense promise, but it is not an alternative to other lines of research. Rather, it is only one additional technique that will supplement more traditional lines of inquiry in the search for the understanding and treatment of psychiatric disorders.' And that comment applies as much to any complex disorder as it does to psychiatric disease.

## Informatics

Research and development generates a vast amount of data that is now well beyond the ability of any one person to evaluate and synthesise. However, in recent years information technology has come to the rescue. Powerful computer bases, working as part of a discipline called informatics, allow researchers to make sense of the growing knowledge base. As Kanehisa, 2000 remarks (p. v): '[I]t is no longer possible to make advances in biology without integration of informatics technologies and experimental technologies.' Indeed, information may be a company's most valuable resource – the recognition of which led to the idea of knowledge management (page 110).

However, informatics aids R&D in two ways. Firstly, informatics can act as a database to support experimenters. There are several databases containing the genetic codes for organisms, for example, which allow researchers to compare their results. Moreover, the European Gene Vector Database and Repository acts, among other things, as a database of knowledge in the literature as well as unpublished practical details for researchers into gene therapy.

Secondly, informatics can synthesise knowledge to take researchers towards an understanding of a system's basic principles and practical applications. For example, researchers can plan new experiments based on this synthetic knowledge. In other words, informatics can help highlight possible new targets for drug development.

## Therapeutic innovation develops new markets

Therapeutic innovation can also help develop new markets. Consider, for example, social phobia. Social phobia 'is the excessive fear that a performance or social interaction will be inadequate, embarrassing, or humiliating' (den Boer, 1997). As a result, sufferers may not be able to eat, talk or even write a cheque in public.

As we mentioned in Chapter 1, the ancients recognised social alienation (Newbold, 1990), a feeling familiar to people with social phobia. However, in 1985, psychiatrists considered social phobia to be an uncommon condition. But today, it seems that the lifetime prevalence is between 2% and 5%, with roughly twice as many women suffering as men (den Boer, 1997). This makes social phobia one of the commonest psychiatric diseases. Healy, 1997 (pp. 188–191) argues that the pace of therapeutic innovation helped to raise awareness of social phobia in among both professionals and the general public.

For example, part of the reason for the growing awareness of social phobia lies in studies suggesting that the condition responds to monoamine oxidase inhibitors, benzodiazepines and, more recently, the selective serotonin reuptake inhibitors (SSRIs). For example, the SSRI paroxetine proved effective in a large-scale placebo-controlled trial (Lydiard, 1998). The monoamine oxidase inhibitor phenelzine, the first drug shown to be effective in social phobia, and the better-tolerated moclobemide and brofaromine are also effective (Noyes et al., 1997). This growing number of drugs meant that doctors could now treat social phobia. Ethically, they could longer either ignore social phobia or dismiss the symptoms as shyness.

Moreover, the fact that a drug treatment was available helped to establish the diagnosis in the minds of the lay public as well as the medical profession. As a result, patients presented for treatment. This sea change in public and professional attitudes gave marketers something to work with. As a result, interest in and awareness of the condition increased rapidly. The social phobia story illustrates the way in which therapeutic studies can help to develop a market.

## The problem with specialisation

The growth in biological knowledge, informatics not withstanding, means that it is now impossible for any one researcher to keep pace with advances in even one relatively tightly defined field – cardiovascular pharmacology, for example. As a result, there is a growing trend towards subspecialisation. One research team may be experts in one receptor system involved in high blood pressure, for example. There are increasing worries that highly specialised research may mean that there is no one left to see the bigger picture or to work at the boundaries between scientific fields, where some of the most interesting advances are made.

Consider the story of *Helicobacter pylori*, for example. Spiral bacteria in the stomach were isolated from mammals in 1874 and humans in 1906. Indeed, some 40% of human stomachs showed the bacteria. However, few scientists believed that bacteria could live in the harsh environment of the stomach. And no one was able to culture the bacterium until Marshall managed the feat in Australia in 1981. Marshall then cultured *H. pylori* from stomach biopsy a year later (Calam, 1996, pp. 1–2). Since then *H. pylori* has been linked to gastric ulcers, stomach cancer and other gastrointestinal diseases. More importantly, combination therapy using omeprazole and other proton pump inhibitors with antibiotics eradicates *H. pylori* and cure the ulcer. In contrast, the $H_2$ antagonists, developed in 1972, only alleviate symptoms.

But the key issue is that the cure for ulcers did not emerge from the gastroenterology research programmes of major academic centres or pharmaceutical companies. As John Calam, a world expert on *H. pylori's* role in gastrointestinal disease, notes (1996, p. 1): 'Major laboratories, by their nature, pursue conventional ideas in great detail. Pharmaceutical companies and peer-reviewed grant-awarding bodies prefer to support elegant studies of more or less conventional ideas .... The message is clear: we do need medical academics, and part of their role is to play the "mad scientist" and explore the unconventional ideas that larger scientific organisations shun.' Losec's position as the world's best selling drug is largely based on an unconventional idea.

Gastrointestinal disease may not be the end of the story. A 1961 paper noted that active ulcers and ulcer-like syndromes were more common in people with Parkinson's disease than in controls. This might be the first hint that *H. pylori* infection is linked to Parkinson's disease. More recent studies support the association, suggesting that the infection can establish a cycle of inflammation leading to autoimmunity and Parkinson's disease (Dobbs *et al.*, 2000). Moreover, there is some evidence – although it is not conclusive – linking infection with *H. pylori* and *Chlamydia pneumoniae* with an increased risk of developing heart disease (Koenig, 2000). This suggests that bacterial infections may be important in the pathogenesis of many common condition and opens up the possibility of innovative therapies.

# Chapter 5: Clinical development

Once a pharmaceutical company develops or licenses a novel compound and once the new drug has undergone extensive *in vivo* and *in vitro* preclinical studies (see Chapter 4), the drug enters a clinical development programme that can last for 5–6 years, or even longer. Usually, clinical trials take place in three prelaunch stages that aim to provide information from the total of 3,000–5,000 patients needed for approval worldwide. About 80% of this patient population takes part in phase III studies. However, there is an increasing move to performing clinical studies after launch. As a result, monitoring drug safety in everyday clinical practice is now increasingly the responsibility of the pharmaceutical industry as well as the regulatory authorities (see page 70 and Chapter 8).

## The cost of clinical development

Performing clinical trials requires a considerable investment of time, money and other resources. Estimates of the exact cost of clinical development vary, depending in part on the accounting methods used and the therapeutic area (Table 5.1). However, around 30% of the total cost of $300m or so that analysts claim companies spend developing a drug funds the clinical trials programme (Walsh, 1998, p. 152). And most of that is spent on the phase III study (Table 5.1). Indeed, a large phase III study that lasts a year and involves up to 1,000 patients can cost between $30m and $50m (Drews, 1999, p. 134). Despite this investment, there is no guarantee that a new drug will make it through the clinical development programme to market. There is a considerable attrition rate (Table 5.2). As a result, most analysts examine the total cost *per approved drug* to allow for expenses incurred in developing drugs that were eventually withdrawn.

### Table 5.1: Out of pocket costs of clinical development in various therapeutic groups (1997, US data)

| Therapeutic area | Expected costs per IND ($m) | | | Success rate (%) | Total clinical costs per approved drug ($m) |
|---|---|---|---|---|---|
| | Phase I | Phase II | Phase III | | |
| NSAID | 4 | 5.3 | 11.2 | 22.2 | 99.5 |
| Cardiovascular | 3.1 | 3.8 | 6.5 | 26.2 | 62.2 |
| Neuropharmacological | 1.5 | 2.7 | 6.3 | 20.3 | 61.1 |
| Anti-infective | 3.1 | 4.1 | 7.0 | 30.2 | 49.0 |
| **Average of all areas** | **2.9** | **4.0** | **6.3** | **23.0** | **64.9** |

IND = investigational new drug; NSAID = nonsteroidal anti-inflammatory drug.

Source: based on Kettler, 1999

## Prelaunch development

The three phases of clinical studies performed prelaunch aim to characterise the new treatments' pharmacological and toxicological properties as well as the appropriate dose, route and frequency of administration. These prelaunch studies

### Table 5.2: The attrition rate for clinical development

| Phase | INDs successful (%) | Probability of entering phase (%) |
|---|---|---|
| I | 70 | 100 |
| II | 33 | 75 |
| III | 25 | 36.2 |
| Registration | 20 | |

Source: based on Kettler, 1999

show that the new drug is well tolerated ('safe') and effective. However, neither efficacy nor tolerability is an absolute.

For example, a drug may be relatively 'well tolerated' if it produces fewer side-effects than conventional agents already on the market. (The current 'best' treatment is known as 'the gold standard'.) Nevertheless, side-effects may still be common. In practice, tolerability means that the drug shows an acceptable risk:benefit ratio for the indication as compared with currently available therapies.

So a drug destined for treating cancer often shows a number of serious side-effects, some of which may even be life threatening. However, as many cancers are usually fatal, the benefits outweigh the risks. On the other hand, a contraceptive pill or prophylactic vaccine that is administered to essentially healthy people needs to be almost devoid of serious adverse events, although a minor injection-site reaction is acceptable. However, vaccine-related brain damage and an increased risk of thrombosis (blood clot) with certain oral contraceptives illustrate that no drug is completely free of side-effects. Against this background, the clinical trials programme aims to characterise the risk:benefit ratio.

Similarly, few drugs are universally effective. For instance, variations in the amount of drug that reaches the site of action and genetically determined differences in the receptors though which the drug exerts its influence can affect a drug's efficacy. Therefore, phase II and especially phase III studies are designed to determine effectiveness in a range of patients. Whether the average effectiveness is acceptable in the current market place depends on the disease.

So, a drug that shows an average effectiveness of 25% in a previously untreatable cancer represents an important therapeutic advance. An efficacy of 25% would be unacceptable for a first-line treatment for high blood pressure (hypertension) when other more effective agents are already on the market. Traditionally, these trials characterise average effectiveness. Advances in genomics mean that doctors may soon be able to stratify patients into those who are likely, based on their genetic profile, to respond to or develop side-effects to a particular drug. This means that future clinical trials may have to stratify patients according to their genetic profile.

Moreover, few drugs cure diseases. There are notable exceptions: antivirals, antibiotics and antifungals usually eradicate the underlying microorganism. This cures the condition. And it is often forgotten that some cancers are curable. Cancer specialists regard the 5-year survival rate as being equivalent to a cure.

After this time, patients' survival prospects are about the same as those of the general population. Today in the best centres, 5-year survival rates for localised prostate, breast and some skin cancers are well over 90%.

On the other hand, drugs for hypertension, asthma and dyslipidaemias (dangerous levels of cholesterol and other lipids in the blood) do not cure the underlying condition, which arises through a combination of genetic and environmental factors. Rather these drugs tackle the associated abnormality – raised blood pressure, lung inflammation and abnormal lipid profiles, respectively. This reduces the likelihood that the person will suffer a serious event arising from the abnormality. However, the underlying cause remains. As a result, if patients stop taking the drug, the abnormality remains and so they remain at risk, provided they remain exposed to the same risk factors. Thus a low fat diet can reduce blood cholesterol levels but few people are able to comply with the severe dietary restrictions required.

The effectiveness of such 'symptomatic' treatments can be difficult to assess in clinical trials. Ideally, the study would look at the drug's effects on the so-called 'hard' endpoints – death or a heart attack, for example. However, such studies tend to be large, expensive and lengthy. So many studies rely on 'surrogate' endpoints. These predict the risk of suffering a hard endpoint either for each patient or from a population perspective. For example, doctors can use objective measures of the drug's effect: a blood pressure reading, lung function test or serum lipid profile. Taken across the whole population these are associated with, for example, a risk of stroke, asthma or heart attack. However, they do not show that any particular patient will indeed develop the disease.

However, some conditions do not lend themselves even to surrogate measures. In some cases, the outcome measures may be subjective – such as a change in patients' and physicians' rating of depression, anxiety and schizophrenia, for example. In others, quality of life may be important. This is especially true of the so-called 'lifestyle' drugs, palliative treatments and some neurological conditions. Nevertheless, quality-of-life considerations are increasingly influential factors in the decision to prescribe in many therapeutic areas.

As a result, a growing number of trials, especially during phases II and III, include quality of life or other questionnaires that allow researchers to gain an insight into the drug's efficacy. So, for example, the severity of Parkinson's disease can be assessed using the Hoehn and Yahr scale. The effectiveness of a drug for anxiety can be measured using the Hamilton anxiety and clinical global impression (CGI) scales. Furthermore, there are now numerous specific, health-related quality-of-life measures for diseases as diverse as asthma and impotence, as well as measures of patients' ability to perform 'activities of daily living'. These last may be used in studies examining the impact of a drug on a neurological disease.

Nevertheless, there can be marked discrepancies between objective and subjective measures of health. For instance, three times as many people in Wales report being permanently sick as those living in south-east England (Rose, 1993, p. 1). While there are real social differences between the richer and poorer parts of most developed counties, including the UK, these could not account for this marked variation. Clearly, such variations could influence patients' responses to quality-of-life measures. But perhaps the best indication that subjective assessments such as quality of life don't directly follow objective outcomes came in the late 1980s when the World Health Organization (WHO) commissioned international Gallup polls of people in several countries. As Table 5.3 shows, there was a marked difference between the numbers reporting that their health was very good – a subjective marker of health status – and life expectancy, perhaps the best objective measure (Rose, 1993, p. 11).

**Table 5.3: Discrepancy between objective and subjective outcome measures**

| Country | 'Health is very good' (%) | Life expectancy (years) |
|---------|---------------------------|-------------------------|
| Ireland | 48 | 71.6 |
| US | 40 | 71.6 |
| UK | 39 | 72.4 |
| Sweden | 38 | 74.2 |
| Australia | 36 | 73.2 |
| France | 19 | 72.6 |
| Italy | 15 | 72.7 |
| Japan | 9 | 75.9 |
| USSR | 3 | 65.1 |

Source: based on Rose, 1993, p. 11

## Paediatric trials

Clinical trials need to reflect the concerns and values of the society for which they are performed. Two examples illustrate this. We will look at some of the ethical considerations in clinical trials generally later (page 68). But before reviewing the main types of clinical trial, it is worth mentioning the growing pressure for increased numbers of paediatric trials, which must follow the phase I–III stages outlined below.

Traditionally, many drugs are not tested in children. There are clearly problems with obtaining informed consent as well as difficulties in coping with the differences in dose, metabolic ability and so on. As a result, paediatric specialists often use drugs off-licence – in other words outside the indications approved by the regulatory authorities. This has led to concern that children may be exposed to unacceptable risks. As a result, in April 1999 the FDA insisted that companies should state whether or not the drug has been subjected to clinical trials in children. Indeed, the FDA now grants a 6-month patent extension to drugs licensed for children (Willis, 2000).

Pressure for increased numbers of paediatric trials is also mounting in the UK and continental Europe. For example, the International Conference on Harmonisation (ICH) – see page 105 – issued draft guideline stating that: '[p]aediatric patients should be given medicines which have been appropriately evaluated for their use…. Drug development programmes should include the paediatric population when a product is being developed for a disease/condition in adults and it is anticipated that the product will be used in the paediatric population.'

Moreover, companies increasingly recognise that children represent a potentially lucrative and, to date, largely untapped market. In the UK, for example, around 25% of the population is under 19 years of age. Meanwhile, in America, some 25 paediatric medicines were approved in 2000, 217 are in development and another 52 should enter clinical trials by the end of 2000. As Table 5.4 shows, these cover a range of indications, although cancer is by far the commonest. In some ways, this is not surprising: paediatric clinical trials are best-established in cancer. Nevertheless, the market for industry-sponsored paediatric studies is growing by around 18% annually. This is some 6% more than the overall market (Willis, 2000).

### Table 5.4: Number and indications of drugs in development for children during 2000

| Indication | No. medicines in development |
| --- | --- |
| Cancer | 48 |
| Cardiovascular disease | 19 |
| Vaccines | 18 |
| Bacterial infections | 15 |
| Psychiatric disorders | 15 |
| Asthma | 14 |
| Respiratory disorders | 13 |
| AIDS and AIDS-related conditions | 9 |
| Neurological disorders | 9 |
| Cystic fibrosis | 7 |
| Genetic disorders | 7 |
| Transplantation | 7 |
| Epilepsy | 6 |
| Gastrointestinal conditions | 6 |
| Eye disorders | 4 |
| Fungal infections | 3 |
| Diabetes | 2 |
| Growth disorders | 2 |
| Dermatological conditions | 2 |
| Juvenile rheumatoid arthritis | 2 |
| Viral infections | 2 |
| Others | 12 |

Some drugs have more than one indication.

Source: adapted from PhRMA, cited in Willis, 2000

## Phase I

During phase I studies, a small number of healthy volunteers – typically between 20 and 80 – takes the drug under very tightly controlled conditions. The phase I trial aims to assess safety by measuring critical physiological parameters, such as blood pressure, heart rate and liver function. As this is the first time humans have taken the drug, and animals are not perfect models, phase I studies are usually performed in special units where volunteers can be closely monitored by specialised doctors or nurses. In many cases, phase I units are attached to teaching hospitals or run by specialised contract companies, who employ experienced clinicians.

To further reduce the risk, volunteers tend to be healthy young men able to assess the risks – for example, healthy volunteer studies often use medical students. They undergo an extensive health check to rule out any diseases and to screen for factors, such as illegal drug use or chronic alcohol abuse, that may increase the risks of the study or compromise the results. However, in some cases, such as cancer, where the drugs are expected to be toxic, phase I studies may enrol terminally ill patients.

Phase I studies begin by administering a very low dose of the drug, below that expected, from the animal studies, to be pharmacologically active. If no adverse events emerge, the dose is gradually increased until minor, acute side-effects – a change in heart rate or an increase in the level of certain liver enzymes – emerges. Once the highest single tolerated dose is known, the researchers test the effects of multiple doses, which are generally somewhat lower than the highest single tolerated dose. However, during phase I studies the duration of treatment is usually short – perhaps a week or so. During this time the volunteers remain in the phase I unit. This reduces the possibility that any outside influences can affect the result.

Usually, the phase I studies last a year or so. During this time, the studies begin to characterise the drug's pharmacokinetics and pharmacodynamics in humans. As a reminder – pharmacokinetic studies aim to characterise how the body handles a drug. So, a pharmacokinetic study characterises the drug's absorption, distribution, metabolism and excretion. In contrast, pharmacodynamic studies characterise the drug's biological effects. So pharmacodynamic studies may explore how the drug interacts with cells – its effects, adverse reactions, dose-response, etc.

---

### Example: A phase I study in cancer

A typical phase I study in cancer (de Jonge *et al.*, 2000) examined a combination of the cancer drugs topotecan and cisplatin. Forty-eight patients took escalating doses for 5 days in a randomised, crossover design (see below) every 3 weeks until they experienced dose-limiting toxicity, in this case bone marrow suppression and diarrhoea. The study also examined the two agents' pharmacokinetics. A phase II study examined the combination's effectiveness against the tumour.

---

## Phase II

During phase II studies, a larger number of patients (perhaps 200–300), who are suffering from the condition for which the drug is indicated, take the medication. The phase II studies aim to assess whether the drug is effective enough to warrant further investigation. They do not give a definitive assessment of the extent of that activity. As a result, phase II studies are often placebo-controlled. In other words, one group of patients receives the test compound while the other group takes an inactive placebo. In some cases, the placebo and test drug are added to the patients' current therapies.

The use of a placebo is, usually, unavoidable. Not treating the patient can mask the 'placebo effect' (see below) arising from being involved in a study, while trials using historical controls are fraught with methodological problems (Lapierre, 1998). For example, more aspects of healthcare may have changed over several years than just the treatment. So disentangling the confounding factors in studies that employ historical controls can be difficult.

On the other hand, using a placebo compensates for any unintentional bias in both patients and doctors, as well as allowing for the power of the mind over the body. If patients believe that the drug may be active, they often feel better and, for example, blood pressure may fall. However, the improvement seen with placebo tends to be shorter lived. If the drug's benefits take a few days or weeks to emerge – as may be the case with antidepressants – the improvement may emerged more rapidly on placebo. The placebo effect occurs to a greater or lesser extent in 60–90% of medical conditions. And the placebo effect is found in all ages, from babies to the elderly, from all cultures (Lapierre, 1998). Moreover, just being involved in a clinical trial, with all the extra attention from medical staff, can lead to a change in the 'therapeutic environment'. This can contribute to the placebo effect.

The phase II studies aim to confirm that the treatment works and does not cause common, unacceptable side-effects. Moreover, phase II studies may explore pharmacokinetics and pharmacodynamics in more detail. For example, some diseases and factors – such as race or age – can alter the pharmacokinetics and pharmacodynamics of a particular drug. Obviously, this would not emerge in the phase I studies, which enrolled healthy young men. Phase II studies can last up to 2 years.

If the company decides to study the agent for additional indications, the clinical development programme needs to begin again at phase II. For example, the original indication for the selective serotonin reuptake inhibitors (SSRIs) – such as Prozac – was depression. Phase I and II studies confirmed their effectiveness in this common condition. However, it soon became clear that SSRIs were also effective in a range of other diseases, including obsessive compulsive disorder, some eating disorders, phobias, and so on. The clinical development for these new indications began again at phase II.

## Example: A phase II study in HIV

A phase II placebo-controlled trial examined the pharmacokinetics, tolerability and efficacy of fozivudine tidoxil, a new treatment for HIV (Girard *et al.*, 2000). A total of 72 HIV-infected patients received various doses of either fozivudine tidoxil or placebo for 4 weeks, added to their current therapy. Overall, fozivudine was well tolerated. One patient discontinued the drug following a moderate rise in levels of a liver enzyme (aminotransaminase). The study used viral load, the number of viral particles in the blood, as a surrogate marker of activity. HIV viral load fell in all patients receiving fozivudine, at all doses except at the lowest. The authors found a relationship between the dose and the extent of the decrease in viral load (the dose–response relationship). This suggests that fozivudine tidoxil may be a promising new treatment for HIV infection. However, this potential needs confirmation in phase III studies.

## Phase III

Phase III studies offer the first real indication of how effective and well-tolerated a drug may be once, and if, it reaches clinical practice. During phase III studies a large number of patients – usually at least several hundred and up to 5,000 or more – receive the drug for a period appropriate to the disease being treated. Given the number of patients involved, and to ensure that a broad selection of patients are included, phase III studies usually involve several hospitals or practices (this is called a multicentre study). Increasingly, these centres are in several countries. Often, companies select the countries in which approval is the most important or which have the largest market.

Apart from meeting the demands of the regulatory authorities, phase III studies offer companies an opportunity to work with opinion leaders. Phase III studies allow the opinion leaders to become familiar with the drug before launch. In many cases, the phase III trialists will act as advocates for the new drug. Their experiences during the phase III studies mean that they will be well placed to inform other clinicians about the agent before, during and after launch.

During the phase III studies, the drug is compared to either an inactive placebo or a better-established treatment. The latter is important if placebo treatment would expose patients to unacceptable risk. However, using another drug (an active comparator) makes assessing the extent of any difference in effect more difficult and, therefore, usually means enrolling more patients than are necessary for a placebo-controlled study. On the other hand, an active comparator can be especially useful if the study aims to examine a drug that should show similar efficacy to the gold standard, but with a lower risk of side-effects. Most modern antihypertensives and antidepressants, for example, are no more effective than the older agents. However, they are less likely to cause side-effects. Therefore, more patients are likely to comply with treatment and benefit from taking the agent.

Typically, the phase III programme may last 3 or more years. Increasingly, companies perform prospective pharmacoeconomic studies (see page 42) based on the phase III population (see below). This reflects the growing importance of NICE, other health technology assessors and some regulatory authorities – such as Australia – which now have either an implicit or explicit 'fourth hurdle' based on cost–effectiveness (see page 42).

The phase III studies will also undergo extensive statistical analysis. For example, the results may be stratified by gender, age and disease. However, to be enrolled in the study, patients typically need to meet a number of inclusion and exclusion criteria. As a result, the findings may not always apply directly to patients seen in the clinic. Moreover, even large phase III studies may not be large enough to accurately assess the risk that some rare side-effects will emerge. These may not become apparent until a large, unselected population uses the drug. Indeed, there have been several cases where a drug was withdrawn after launch because of such side-effects despite showing a good tolerability profile during the phase III studies.

## Study design

Phase II and III studies can follow several designs. However, the randomised controlled study has been the design of choice for almost 40 years. Following the

CLINICAL DEVELOPMENT

## Example: The 4S study

The Scandinavian Simvastatin Survival Study (4S), published in 1994, is one of the few studies to have transformed the management of a common condition. Studies published before 4S indicated a link (association) between raised cholesterol levels and an increased risk of developing heart disease. But these studies relied on surrogate outcome markers (see above). In contrast, the 4S study showed for the first time that lowering levels of cholesterol reduced the morbidity and mortality (so-called hard outcome measures) associated with heart disease.

The study treated 4,444 patients, who either suffered from angina or had experienced a heart attack, with either simvastatin or placebo. At this time there was no proof that lowering cholesterol reduced the morbidity and mortality associated with heart disease. Therefore, a placebo arm was ethical. It is unlikely that it would be acceptable for a study of a cholesterol-lowering agent starting today.

During 4S, researchers followed patients for an average of 5.4 years. Over this time, 12% of the placebo group died, compared to 8% of those taking simvastatin. The study also found that simvastatin reduced coronary deaths, nonfatal events and the need for bypass surgery.

During 4S researchers prospectively collected information on resource use. Based on this, Johannesson and colleagues (1997) estimated the cost per year of life gained from simvastatin, including both direct and indirect costs (see below) at various ages and total cholesterol levels. The cost of each year of life gained ranged from $3,800 for 70-year-old men with blood cholesterol levels of 309 mg/dl (milligrams per 100 millilitres) to $27,400 for 35-year-old women with cholesterol levels of 213 mg/dl. Including indirect costs, the analysis found that reducing cholesterol reduced cost in younger patients but increased expenditure in the elderly.

thalidomide tragedy, the US congress passed the Kefauver–Harris amendments in 1962. These aimed to increase the rigour with which pharmaceutical companies tested their products. For example, one amendment institutionalised the randomised placebo-controlled, double-blind study as 'the appropriate means, indeed, almost the only scientific means' of establishing efficacy (Healy, 1997, p. 26). This view has remained largely unchallenged for almost 40 years.

During a randomised controlled study, a group of patients who meet certain inclusion and exclusion criteria have an equal chance of being assigned to any one of the test groups. The group they end up in is purely a matter of chance. This 'randomisation' should minimise any unintentional bias by the study investigators. Usually, such studies are also 'blinded'. When neither the patient nor the investigator knows which treatment the patient is receiving, the study is 'double blind'. When either the clinician or the patient does not know, the study is 'single blind'. Again, blinding a study minimises the risk of bias.

However, a blinded study is not always possible, e.g. if a study is comparing two different delivery devices in asthma. In such cases, it is impracticable for patients to learn to use both inhalers, which might employ very different techniques. Or the rival manufacturer might not agree to supply a placebo version of an inhaler. Trials in which both patient and clinician know that the drug or treatment they are taking is the one under trial are called open studies.

Some phase II and, less commonly, phase III studies use a crossover design. In these studies, patients receive one of, usually, two treatments or a placebo. After an appropriate time, they cross over to the next treatment, and so on, so that eventually all the patients have received all the treatments. This is a powerful design that allows researchers to accurately assess a drug's effectiveness and tolerability in a relatively small number of patients.

## The ethics of clinical trials

As mentioned several times during the book, biomedical research cannot – and should not – take place in an ethical vacuum. Nowhere is this clearer than in research on humans. It is an area fraught with difficulty. Archie Cochrane, who largely pioneered the use of randomised controlled trials, eventually took the view that any trial that was publicly acceptable was ethical (Rose, 1993, p. 107). Yet, to be publicly acceptable a study needs to take place within a legal and ethical framework.

The ethics of clinical trials are regulated on principles laid down in the Declaration of Helsinki, commonly known as the Helsinki Agreement. The original agreement arose from the Nuremberg trials in the autumn of 1947, which covered, among other things, the abuse of prisoners by the Nazis in purportedly scientific medical trials. The trials led to the Nuremberg codes, which formally established ethical standards that researchers should meet. The Helsinki Agreement followed in 1964 and was the first attempt to formulate a universal code to control medical studies. The Helsinki Agreement was amended in 1975, 1983, 1989 and 1996. It is currently undergoing revision again to take account of the genomics revolution.

Through its numerous clauses, the Declaration of Helsinki aims to ensure that, for example, considerations related to the wellbeing of subjects take precedence over the interests of science and society. The Declaration also points out that medical research is only justified if there is a reasonable likelihood that the populations in which the research is carried out stand to benefit from the results of the research.

The Declaration is implemented nationally. In the US, for example, federally funded and regulated clinical trials are approved by an Institutional Review Board (IRB), which consists of scientists, physicians and local laypeople. These boards review the study before it begins, to ensure that the subjects' rights are well protected and that the benefits outweigh the risks. Similarly, in the UK, most hospitals have an ethics committee that ensures that a study conforms to the standards set out in the declaration.

Under the Helsinki Agreement, patients need to sign an 'informed consent' form stating that they understand the study's nature, potential benefits and risks, as well as their rights and responsibilities. Informed consent is a cornerstone of ethical clinical trials. Thus researchers tend to avoid enrolling patients who are in dependent relationships or extending any undue influence or duress. This principle of informed consent is one reason why so few paediatric studies have been performed. It may, however, be less of a hindrance than it appears. Even patients seriously ill with schizophrenia are often 'competent to consent to treatment' according to the law (Addington, 1995). Nevertheless, the fact that informed consent has been given does not abrogate clinicians from their responsibility for ensuring that the other ethical principles are followed during this study.

Informed consent is now well established as a cornerstone of medical ethics, both in drug trials and in medical care more generally. However, the ethics of clinical trials dictate that the patient should not be exposed to 'unacceptable risk'. Moreover, any risks need to be balanced against the benefits. Informed consent does not mean that the patient accepts *any* level of risk. So the Nuremberg declaration states that: 'the experiment should be so conducted as to avoid all unnecessary physical and mental suffering and injury ... the degree of risk to be taken should never exceed that determined by the humanitarian importance of the problem to be solved by the experiment' (Young, 1998).

Similarly, the Helsinki Agreement states that 'biomedical research involving human subjects cannot legitimately be carried out unless the importance of the objective is in proportion to the inherent risk to the subject'. The declaration adds that, while: 'every biomedical research project involving human subjects should be preceded by careful assessment of predictable risks in comparison with foreseeable benefits to the subject, or to others ... concern for the interests of the subject must always prevail over the interests of science and society' (Young, 1998). Clearly, however, both offer scope for interpretation. The local ethics committees and IRB help to ensure that the interpretation is fair and consistent.

Moreover, researchers are under an obligation to ensure that the study is performed to a high standard. Obviously, the sponsoring pharmaceutical company also has a vested interest in ensuring that the study is of high quality, especially as it will undergo intensive scrutiny by regulatory authorities to ensure its validity. Good Clinical Practice (GCP) is an internationally agreed set of rules and regulations that ensures that the study is performed to a high standard, overseen by the ICH (page 105). GCP is defined as 'a standard for the design, conduct, performance, monitoring, auditing, recording, analyses and reporting of clinical trials that provides assurance that the data and results are credible and accurate, and that the rights, integrity and confidentiality of trial subjects are protected'. For instance, researchers must follow standard operating procedures (SOPs) for routine tasks, there is a detailed protocol, and every result must be traceable to the original observation (this is called an audit trail). Moreover, the trial must be examined in minute detail by a clinical research associate (CRA), either from the sponsoring company or a specialised contract company.

## Postlaunch clinical trials

Only between 10% and 20% of new drugs that enter phase I clinical trials reach the market (Walsh, 1998, p. 56). However, launch is not the end of a company's clinical research responsibilities. Increasingly, a drug still faces considerable scrutiny once it reaches the market, both from the company and from the regulatory authorities (see Chapter 8). Furthermore, health technology assessors – such as the UK's NICE – look for a new type of data that isn't required by many regulatory authorities. For example, health technology assessors want data about the drug's impact in naturalistic practice, such as, if appropriate, the effect on nurse triage systems and doctors' surgeries. Phase IV studies can provide marketing ammunition, especially in crowded markets.

Against this background, phase IV studies take place after the drug is launched. During phase IV studies, large numbers of patients – often enrolled from general practices or local, rather than teaching, hospitals – take the medication to assess its effectiveness and safety in the 'real world'. Clinical trials generally have a large number of inclusion and exclusion criteria. This means that many of the people likely to use a drug, such as the elderly and those with other (concurrent) diseases, may be excluded. Phase IV studies enrol everyone who takes the medication.

---

### Example: Phase IV studies and antifungals

One phase IV study (Binder and Nell, 1999) assessed the oral antifungal terbinafine. The study enrolled 454 patients with superficial fungal infections, such as onychomycosis (fungal nail infection), from 79 dermatology clinics across several countries. Patients were examined before and after two week's treatment. This revealed that overall clinical efficacy was assessed as good-to-excellent in 97% of patients. Around 5% reported adverse effects. The study broadly confirms findings in earlier clinical studies.

---

## Safety assessment of marketed medicines

Safety assessment of marketed medicines (SAMM) studies take phase IV studies a stage further by enrolling many thousands of patients. This helps to identify rare, unexpected side-effects. Moreover, SAMM studies augment postmarketing surveillance and pharmacovigilance procedures, many of which arose from government attempts to avoid a repeat of the thalidomide tragedy. As the latter are mainly the responsibility of the regulatory authorities, they are covered in Chapter 8.

---

### Example: SAMM and environmentally friendly inhalers

Under international law, environmentally friendly hydrofluoroalkane (HFA) propellants must replace chlorofluorocarbons (CFCs), which damage the ozone layer, in all commercial applications, including healthcare products. As chlorofluorocarbons are used in metered dose inhalers, the mainstay of therapy in around 70% of asthma patients across the industrialised world, the replacement needed to be safe. An extensive clinical and preclinical programme, in which several large companies collaborated, suggested that the hydrofluoroalkanes were safe. Indeed, the new hydrofluoroalkane propellant was more extensively tested than its predecessor.

This safety profile was confirmed in a SAMM study (Ayres *et al.*, 1998) that compared patients taking metered doses of salbutamol (which dilates the airways, thereby relieving the asthma attack) delivered by inhalers using either hydrofluoroalkane or chlorofluorocarbon as the propellant. The study examined 6,614 patients with obstructive airways disease (such as asthma) from 646 general practices throughout the UK. This meant that there was a total of 1,667 patient years of exposure. The hydrofluoroalkane inhaler emerged as being as safe as the chlorofluorocarbon inhaler when judged by hospital admissions and side-effects. This type of study offers a degree of reassurance that is impossible to attain in other clinical trials.

---

## Health economics

As healthcare budgets come under increasing scrutiny, health economics – also called pharmacoeconomics when the focus is predominately on a drug's impact on overall costs – is becoming an increasingly important part of clinical development. Indeed, pharmacoeconomic studies increasingly influence whether or not a candidate molecule progresses through development.

Moreover, several countries now have a formal or informal 'fourth hurdle' that a drug needs to clear: any drug needs to show that it is cost-effective as well as clinically effective, well tolerated and of high quality before it is widely used. This is more than price (acquisition cost): a cheap drug may cost the health service more if it is less effective or causes expensive-to-treat side-effects, for example. Health economics is a complex, increasingly sophisticated and rapidly evolving discipline. However, there are essentially four types of study:

*Cost–benefit analyses* evaluate, usually in monetary terms, all or as many as possible of the costs and consequences associated with a healthcare programme such as a new drug or a novel operation. As a result, cost–benefit studies include the direct and indirect costs (see below) and evaluate all the gains, benefits and losses associated with the competing treatments. They could be used to look at the total cost of treatment with a drug for multiple sclerosis, for example.

*Cost-minimisation analyses* compare drugs that produce the same outcomes but at different costs. While cost-minimisation analyses are the simplest economic evaluations to perform, few agents produce the same outcomes in terms of effectiveness and side-effects. However, a cost-minimisation analysis may be appropriate if the researcher wants to compare, for example, two related calcium antagonists or NSAIDs.

*Cost-effectiveness analyses* compare programmes that have the same objective but different effectiveness. So, cost-effectiveness analyses might compare two treatments for depression or schizophrenia from different chemical classes and with a different profile of benefits and risks. The ratio between the two (the incremental cost-effectiveness) allows clinicians to compare the 'value for money' of the two regimens. The cost per life year gained is commonly used in some diseases, e.g. cancer and heart disease, as in the 4S economic analysis mentioned above (page 66).

---

### Example: Cost-effectiveness in cervical cancer

Rose and Lappas (2000) conducted a pharmacoeconomic analysis to compare two regimens for cervical cancer. They estimated that the cost per year of life gained for cisplatin added to radiation regimens varied from $2,384 to $28,770 (based on published survival) when compared to radiotherapy alone. In other words, patients gain life, but at a cost. This is the usual outcome of health economic assessments: the outcome is better, but at a price.

---

It is important to understand that cost-effectiveness studies only offer an insight into the relative costs of treatment. They do not show whether investing in the treatment is worthwhile given the competing demands on the healthcare budget. For example, the cost per year of life gained in the cervical cancer study is roughly the same as the 4S analysis above. So, if you could fund only one, would you treat cervical cancer or heart disease? Such dilemmas are at the heart of the debate about cost effectiveness and healthcare funding currently taking place worldwide. And these debates influence the dynamics of the pharmaceutical market.

*Cost–utility analyses* aim to assess the patient's wellbeing, perhaps using a quality of life measure that assesses subjective improvements or an activities of daily living scale. Performing a cost–utility analysis allows economists to derive a QALY (quality adjusted life year). Death or a year in a coma is defined as 0 QALY, while a year in perfect health is 1 QALY. Cost–utility studies often compare the cost per QALY gained. Moreover, the approach allows healthcare managers to compare different strategies – such as counselling cigarette smokers, bypass operations and breast cancer treatments, for example. However, QALYs have been criticised for being racist, sexist and ageist, partly because the value attached to a life is, to a certain extent, based on the ability to work and economic performance.

These different approaches can include three main types of cost:

* *Direct costs* – costs incurred organising and working a healthcare programme. So direct costs may include physician time, drug costs, the cost of tests, travel time for patients, etc. Often, however, studies focus on direct costs to the healthcare system alone, which may not paint the whole picture.

* *Indirect costs* – the cost to society in, for example, lost or gained productivity. Often the indirect costs impose a heavier burden on society than direct costs alone. There are other indirect costs, such as those arising through lost interest and the costs incurred by carers. Indirect costs are of increasing interest. Some drugs – such as those for multiple sclerosis (MS), Alzheimer's disease and some cancers – may have their greatest economic impact on areas outside the narrow health budget. For instance, a drug for MS or cancer may be expensive to the health service but, because it allows people to remain at work longer, the increased cost is more than offset by tax revenues. Similarly, long-term residential care is one of the most expensive aspects of management. Therefore, a treatment that shortens the duration of residential care is likely to reduce the overall cost of a condition to society. Nevertheless, in many counties the budgets for social care and healthcare, let alone general taxation, are separate. As a result, analyses based on these factors may be less influential among most doctors and healthcare managers than direct health service costs.

* *Intangible costs* – the emotions and social costs involved, such as pain, broken relationships and lost potential. Clearly, it is hard to put an economic cost on, for example, the pain of terminal cancer or the lost potential that arises from schizophrenia.

## Transparency

As a growing number of studies are performed globally, there is an increasing demand for regulatory transparency. In other words, the regulatory authorities of one country should recognise the studies performed in another. In most cases, the authorities should assume that there is no difference in the effectiveness and safety of the drug between countries. While this poses few problems in Europe, which already has a mutual recognition procedure, it can cause problems between continents (see Chapter 8).

Critics of the need for country-specific studies argue that, in some cases, these differences amount to little more than a policy of protectionism. Some countries have been accused of deciding that they want studies in their population in order

## Example: Direct and indirect costs in Parkinson's disease

A recent study assessed the direct and indirect costs based on questionnaires completed by 440 Parkinson's disease patients who had suffered from the condition for an average of just over 7 years (the duration varied from 0–30 years). The analysis took a comprehensive view of costs, including NHS, social services and private expenditure among the direct costs, while the indirect costs included lost earnings, lost leisure time and costs incurred by carers.

The study showed that the mean direct annual costs per patient rose from around £4,000 among Parkinson's disease sufferers aged less than 65 years to £9,400 among patients over 85 years of age. But when the analysis included indirect costs, patients under 65 years of age proved the most expensive, with the total annual burden reaching £12,700. Indeed, among younger Parkinson's patients, lost earnings emerged as the main cost driver, while long-term institutional care was the main driver among older patients.

On average, NHS costs and social services costs accounted for 38% and 35% respectively of the direct costs associated with Parkinson's disease. Costs rose as symptom severity, measured according to the Hoehn and Yahr scale, worsened. The mean cost at stages 0–1 was around £3,000, compared to about £18,400 at stage 5, a more than fivefold difference. Moreover, the NHS accounted for 65% of direct costs among patients less than 65 years of age compared to 21% among those older than this. Social services costs also rose markedly with severity, from £801 per year at stages 0 and 1 to £7,320 at stage 5.

Overall, drugs account for 11% of overall costs among younger Parkinson's disease patients and 6% among the older patients. But the importance of drugs declined as severity worsened. Drugs accounted for 58% of the total cost of £1,402 at stage 0 and 1, compared to 25% of £4,076 at stage 5. In contrast, secondary care accounted for an increasing proportion of the costs as severity worsened, rising from 27% at stages 0 and 1 to 62% at stage 5. Similarly, patients' expenses rose from £768 at stage 0 and 1 to £6,961 at stage 5.

The study hinted at a strategy that might help to contain costs. Direct costs among patients cared for at home were only 22% of those in long-term institutional care. Indeed, the analysis found that moving to long-term care increased costs by around £11,600 annually. Clearly, any drug that prevents or delays the need for long-term care could make a dramatic impact – not to mention improving quality of life (Greener, 2000c).

to erect a barrier to imports and protect their pharmaceutical industry. However, there are also biologically valid reasons for a lack of transparency, at least between some countries. One of the best studied examines genetically determined variations in the main group of enzymes responsible for metabolising drugs in the liver – the cytochrome p450 family.

For example, the lower mean activity of one of these enzymes – CYP2D6 – in many Orientals underlies the slower metabolism of antidepressants and neuroleptics found in this population and the lower approved dosages. Similarly, diazepam is partially metabolised by another member of the cytochrome p450 family – CYP2C19. A common mutation in Orientals may underlie the slower metabolism of diazepam and a requirement for lower doses compared to Caucasians. Moreover, CYP2C19 mutations may underlie the higher clearance of the ulcer-healing drug omeprazole in Caucasians compared to Chinese and Koreans. Clearly, in such cases you cannot extrapolate from one country to another. Nevertheless, carefully designed phase III studies that include sufficient numbers of these different groups, as well as phase I and II trials that fully characterise the pharmacokinetic and pharmacodynamic differences, should enhance transparency.

## Developing line extensions

Once a drug has jumped all four hurdles, companies are obviously keen to maximise the return on their investment. We will look at marketing in the next chapter. However, development scientists also look to develop line extensions that build on the success of the initial formulation and extent the life cycle (see page 86). At its simplest, a line extension can be a new presentation at a different dose or in a different formulation. Thus, an NSAID can be reformulated as a topical cream, effervescent tablets, a suspension or a suppository. Indeed, 'retroformulation', where a product at the peak of its life cycle is reformulated in a sustained-release product, is now a mainstay of marketing strategy. Other line extensions depend on changing the packaging, such as repackaging as a calendar pack.

Another way to develop a line is to explore new indications that emerge from basic research or clinical observations. The growth of the indications for SSRIs from depression into a variety of other areas is perhaps the best example of this. However, even the humble aspirin received a new lease of life when in 1984 the FDA approved it for the prevention of heart attacks in men who had already suffered an infarct, stroke or angina attacks (Mann and Plummer, 1991, p. 4).

### The importance of the delivery device

Increasingly, however, development scientists are examining novel, high-tech delivery devices to extend the life span of a drug. During the 1970s and 1980s, many drugs were reformulated in sustained-release formulations that reduced the need to take medications frequently. In certain areas – such as hypertension – long-acting drugs, either because of their pharmacokinetic profile or because of their formulation, are now the norm.

Nevertheless, delivery devices can help solve clinicians' day-to-day problems. Compliance is notoriously poor among people with schizophrenia, for example. An innovative new formulation of the atypical antipsychotic olanzapine (Zyprexa VeloTab) dissolves in the mouth. Zyprexa VeloTab, introduced by Eli Lilly in the UK early in 2000, should improve compliance among people who are either unable or reluctant to swallow a standard tablet and might be especially useful in the management of acute symptoms.

Certainly, there are good commercial reasons to develop innovative delivery systems. They may attract a premium price, offer a point of differentiation in crowded markets and extend product life cycle. In the UK, the price differential between standard and sustained-release medications, a marker of the added value derived from the drug delivery technology, ranges from 20% to 100%. Furthermore, many of the new drug-delivery systems help R&D to deliver the fruits of their labour – especially peptides and proteins – without resorting to painful injections. For example, PowderJect Pharmaceuticals specialises in needle-free, pain-free injection of drugs, biopharmaceuticals and vaccines. Its system uses a brief burst of helium to accelerate fine particles of drug to high velocity. As a result, PowderJect systems deliver pharmaceuticals and vaccines without pain and without using needles. Another approach – already marketed for some drugs for migraine and bone disease – uses nasal delivery (see box).

---

### Example: Nasal delivery

Currently, there are two leading niche companies developing novel nasal delivery systems. First, West Pharmaceuticals has several strings to its development bow. For example, it recently started US clinical studies evaluating leuprolide in endometriosis and is preparing European registration documents before entering co-development deals. The company is also developing nasal morphine, which rapidly relives pain and shows a profile similar to intravenous formulations. Clinical testing is under way. The other major niche player – Nastech – is also developing an intranasal morphine formulation as well as, among other things, apomorphine for sexual dysfunction and scopolamine for motion sickness.

---

Lung delivery of proteins and other systemically active drugs is another approach that will become increasingly commonplace over the next few years. Everyone is familiar with inhaled drug delivery for asthma and anaesthetics. However, inhaled delivery offers an effective way to deliver systemically active macromolecules, especially proteins and peptides. These platforms may be suitable for a variety of products, including growth hormone and other peptides. But inhaled insulin will probably be the first to reach the market: it is being developed by Pfizer, Aventis, Novo-Nordisk and Eli Lilly, among others. Inhalation is expected to become a mainstream delivery system for macromolecules over the next few years.

Often, niche companies patent a device that can deliver a number of drugs and develop this technology. The developing company then licenses the device to large pharmaceutical companies. However, such niche companies can evolve into mainstream pharmaceutical companies. Élan offers a case in point. Its Pharmaceutical Technologies arm made a major contribution to the company's rapid and considerable growth. Élan Pharmaceutical Technologies uses proprietary technologies 'to develop, market, and license drug delivery products to its pharmaceutical clients'. Élan developed its first drug delivery technology, SODAS, in the 1970s. Since then it has developed more than 20 marketed products, mainly using innovative oral drug delivery systems. Today, Élan is a successful medium-sized, mainstream pharmaceutical company with an innovative R&D pipeline. In other words, drug delivery systems hone your products' competitive advantage and contribute to your company's growth.

## Clinical trials outsourcing

Managing phase I and II studies is straightforward. They enrol a limited number of patients, tend to be performed in a single unit and usually use experienced investigators. In contrast, phase III and IV studies can prove a logistical nightmare. They tend to be performed in several hospitals or clinics. Any failure to recruit the appropriate number of patients or delays can cost the sponsoring company hundreds of thousands of pounds, dollars or yen. As a result, an industry has grown up to serve the needs of pharmaceutical companies. For example, clinical research organisations (CROs) control the day-to-day management of clinical studies for their client companies. They ensure that the clinicians involved in the study enrol sufficient patients and keep to the dates specified. They also train clinicians in the principles of GCP (page 69).

Sales in the CRO market have increased markedly over the last decade, reaching some $5bn by 1998. Indeed, about 30% of R&D expenditure is now outsourced and the global market increased by 31% in 1999. This rate of growth will slow, analysts predict, to around 18% in 2003. The slowdown will be more marked in the US than in Europe, which account for 60% and 36% of the world market respectively. The slowdown reflects the fact that there is a limit to the extent to which drug companies can – or want to – outsource. Most companies feel they need to retain a certain level of core competency. However, CROs will remain an important partner for pharmaceutical companies.

Currently, Quintiles and Covanc lead the CRO market, with 24% and 15% of the market in 1998. Parexel, PPD, ClinTrials and Kendall are ranked between 3 and 6, accounting for 15% of the clinical research organisation market between them. Overall, the top six companies account for 54% of the world market. Moreover, companies tend to outsource phase II and IV studies (49% of trial expenditure) as well as data management and analysis (29%). Phase I and regulatory affairs are less important in terms of sales. However, these tend to be the cheaper parts of prelaunch development.

Quintiles is now the world-leading CRO – indeed, it is now bigger than many of its clients. Founded in 1982, Quintiles now has more than 20,000 employees in 31 countries. The company offers a broad range of integrated product development and commercialisation services, including:

- Preclinical services

- Clinical trials management

- Data management and biostatistics

- Centralised clinical trial laboratory services

- Formulation and packaging of clinical trial materials

- Pharmaceutical sales and marketing support

- Health management services

- Postsubmission studies in support of marketing claims

- Healthcare policy consulting

- Health information management services

- Strategic medical communication and marketing services

- Development of proprietary software to streamline drug development.

Quintiles – a *Fortune* 1000 company – may be the biggest CRO. However, many other consultancies worldwide focus on one or more of these areas. Certainly, there is increasing demand for CRO services. Quintiles's compound average annual revenue growth rate – which acts as a barometer for the sector – has increased by almost 50% annually over the last 5 years.

Site management organisations (SMOs) are a more recent development that work for both CROs and directly for drug companies. SMOs manage networks of hospitals, primary care practices or specialist clinics that collaborate to enrol patients and perform trials. As such, SMOs offer their clients several benefits. First, sponsors have a single point of access to every hospital, department and practice within the network. Second, SMOs can rapidly identify and assess potential investigators. Third, SMOs maintain ongoing on-site support. Obviously, it would not be financially viable for a sponsor to maintain this level of oversight.

Clearly, taking a drug through clinical development requires a considerable investment of time, money and other resources. At best, only one in five drugs tested in phase I will make it through to the market. However, the best-characterised, best-studied drug may still not make a profit.

# Chapter 6: Manufacturing

Traditionally, pharmaceutical manufacturing has a lower profile – inside and outside the industry – than R&D, the clinical trials programme or marketing. However, manufacturing's low profile does not reflect its central importance as a driver of the company's success. Indeed, manufacturing is the key to the short-term success of most conventional pharmaceutical companies because it ensures cash flow. Without manufacturing, the company wouldn't have any funds to invest in R&D. Without manufacturing, phase II and III studies, which require large quantities of any new drug, would be impossible. Indeed, without manufacturing, there would be no drug to market.

In some cases, manufacturing can directly contribute to the company's profitability. Parts of the manufacturing process, especially for novel drug delivery technology and if special machinery is involved, may be patentable. This offers companies another method of protecting their intellectual property. Indeed, the complexities of modern pharmaceutical manufacturing, especially in drug delivery technology and biopharmaceuticals, mean that this gambit may become increasingly common. It may offer an indirect way to extend the product's life cycle.

And manufacturing is not the poor intellectual relation of R&D and marketing. The scale-up from research to manufacturing quantities means more than a simple multiplication on the back of an envelope. The amounts of raw material involved can be enormous. Making 1 kg of a recombinant biopharmaceutical may take up to 30,000 litres of water, for example (Walsh, 1998, p. 87). Moreover, the quality of the water needs to be better than that of drinking water – in pharmaceutical manufacturing, the latter is suitable only for cleaning noncritical machinery. Furthermore, some stages of a product's manufacture may need to be performed in areas where the air is virtually free of particles and the operators may need to wear special clothes with their own air supply. This raises obvious logistical challenges.

Clearly, maintaining manufacturing conditions that are critical to, for example, ferment a biopharmaceutical is far more difficult on an industrial scale than in a test tube. In many cases, the company may need to develop new machines and technologies to produce industrial quantities of a product. This is one reason why the cost of some biopharmaceuticals is so high and why, in some cases, especially during the clinical trials programme or early in market, supplies may be limited. In some cases, the company's ability to manufacture the new product determines the countries in which it is launched, rather than any commercial considerations.

To make matters even more difficult for the chemical engineers, drug manufacturing is among the most regulated and tightly controlled of any industrial process. Indeed, to gain a product licence, the manufacturer needs to show that the drug is effective and safe – and that manufacturing is safe and of high quality. This means that the manufacturer must use high-quality materials and the process needs to adhere to exacting standards through production from the sourcing of raw materials to distribution to pharmacists and doctors. As discussed in Chapter 1, the forerunners of today's multinational companies depended on their ability to produce high-quality pharmaceuticals. So in some ways little has changed. However, one thing *has* changed: manufacturing companies now have to comply with strict environmental rules covering waste disposal and pollution.

Furthermore, manufacturing cannot rest on its laurels once the product licence has been granted. The site may be inspected at any time and, in some cases, closed by the regulatory authorities. These regulations aim to ensure that each and every batch – indeed each and every vial and each and every tablet – is of the same high quality. Working in pharmaceutical manufacturing is a demanding, challenging job that requires constant vigilance by dedicated personal with an eye for detail. Yet sometimes manufacturing does not receive the accolades it warrants.

A detailed discussion of the chemical engineering intricacies of drug manufacturing is outside the scope of this book. (If you are interested, read some of the standard texts. Walsh, 1998, Chapter 3 offers an informative, detailed consideration of the manufacture of biopharmaceuticals, for example.) Rather, this chapter aims to introduce the regulatory framework within which a drug company needs to work to ensure that its products complete clinical trials and reach the market and to maintain the supplies needed in other parts of the company. Anyone who works in the pharmaceutical sector should try to visit the manufacturing site at least once. It is an eye-opening experience.

## Keeping to standard

Essentially, pharmaceutical manufacturing takes place in two stages. First, primary manufacturing combines and processes raw materials to make the active ingredient. The active ingredient can make up a tiny amount of the final product. A milligram (mg) is a thousandth of a gram. So in a tablet containing 10 mg of a drug there is only a hundredth of a gram of active ingredient. During secondary manufacture, therefore, the active ingredient is mixed with inactive ingredients, called excipients, to give the tablet the correct size, shape and so on. While excipients are pharmacologically inactive, they can, in rare cases, cause allergic or toxic reactions. As a result, any excipients also go through rigorous safety testing. The final formulation is also tested to ensure that it remains stable during storage and does not harbour bacterial growth.

As mentioned above, pharmaceutical manufacturing uses high-quality materials and each step in the process follows exacting standards. As a result, some companies decide against investing in the plant, premises and personnel needed to meet these standards. Instead, they contact out at least some stages of the process to a third party. Some companies contact out the entire manufacturing. Others contact out a single step. The latter is especially common if the delivery device is novel or the machinery is too expensive in terms of the volume of work required for the sponsor to develop it. Thus the formulation of inhaled drugs for asthma or prefilled syringes is often licensed out, for example. Similarly, some companies outsource packaging of certain products.

Whether manufacturing is outsourced or retained in house, the process needs to meet certain legally enforceable standards. These are described either in dedicated documents that form part of the product licence application or in pharmacopoeias that establish manufacturing standards for generic drugs and raw materials. Pharmacopoeias offer an authoritative statement of the quality that a product is expected to meet. Any company holding the relevant manufacturing and marketing licences can manufacture generics, on the basis of the pharmacopoeia monographs – which are publicly available and legally enforceable. As such, the standards laid out in the pharmacopoeia complement and assist licensing and on-going inspection by regulatory authorities. While several countries now have local pharmacopoeias, the *United States Pharmacopeia*, *British Pharmacopoeia* and *European Pharmacopoeia* are the most influential (Drews, 1999, p. 76). For drugs that are still under patent protection, regulatory authorities approve the specific manufacturing processes in, as mentioned above, the product licence application.

## Good Manufacturing Practice

Whether a company manufacturers the oldest generic or the most high-tech biopharmaceutical, it needs to follow Good Manufacturing Practice (GMP). As a result, everyone who works in the pharmaceutical industry should be familiar with the principles of GMP.

GMP places the company under a legal obligation to ensure that the manufacturing processes and operations reach a certain minimum standard. Moreover, regulatory authorities ensure that the company enforces these standards through regular site inspections (see box). Indeed, the authorities may

---

### The MCA's inspector calls

This box briefly summarises the approach of the Medicines Control Agency (MCA) to inspection and enforcement. While the MCA regulates the UK's pharmaceutical industry, a broadly similar approach is used in other countries in the developed world.

The MCA's Inspection and Enforcement Division of 116 staff ensures that the manufacture and distribution of a drug are of a satisfactory quality and comply with the product licence. For example, the Medicines Inspectorate performs on-site inspections to ensure that companies comply with GMP as well as the processing and control details set out in the product licence. The MCA's Inspection and Enforcement Division also inspects:

- Wholesalers for compliance with Good Distribution Practice
- Manufacturers in third countries exporting to the UK
- Importers
- Contract analysts who perform quality control tests.

A company can also request inspection and certification to GMP standards. Companies supplying raw materials or products used in clinical trials might request an inspection, for example. This helps the company to sell its services to clients: it is a mark of quality.

Finally, the MCA's Inspection and Enforcement Division monitors the quality of medicines available on the market and assesses reports of suspected defective products. The MCA analyses around 3,000 samples each year taken from wholesalers, community pharmacies, referred by a pharmacy, hospital, another part of the agency, etc. The agency will discuss results with manufacturers and, if necessary, suggest improvements.

---

close manufacturing sites that fail to make the grade. In some cases, refurbishment or new processes may be sufficient to meet the requirements. The factory can stay open in the meantime. And it is not only small generic houses that have fallen victim to inspectors. The regulatory authorities have, on occasion, closed – at least temporarily – premises owned by some of the world's largest pharmaceutical companies.

The requirements are comprehensive. The following outline is based on the EU's GMP requirements. However, similar principles apply elsewhere in the world, reflecting the global pharmaceutical marketing base as well as increasing harmonisation. The EU also publishes a number of annexes covering specific issues such as the preparation of sterile products, herbal medicines and pressurised metered dose inhalers.

## Quality management

A management system to ensure that each batch of a pharmaceutical is of high quality needs to be in place and, importantly, verifiably *seen* to be in place. Furthermore, quality management aims to drive a continual improvement in the standards that the company works to.

This means ensuring that a well-defined line of quality management is in place from the time the company sources the raw material to the delivery of the product to the pharmacist or hospital. For example, the quality management system ensures that the correct procedures – often defined in standard operating procedures (SOPs) – are in place and that there are adequate checks and controls throughout manufacturing and distribution. Moreover, the company needs to be able to show the regulatory authorities that it has followed the appropriate processes with due care and diligence.

### Personnel

Manufacturing's quality depends, to a large part, on the quality of its personnel. The company needs to employ adequate numbers of staff who are appropriately qualified, well trained and work to defined job descriptions. Moreover, the organisational structure must reflect the need to ensure effective quality management. For example, the head of production and head of quality control should be independent.

Moreover, every person involved in manufacturing must maintain high standards of hygiene appropriate to his/her job. This is true of everyone who could potentially contaminate pharmaceutical manufacturing, including contract cleaners, for example. Some areas, of course, need higher hygiene standards than others. For example, drugs intended for systemic injection could also inject virus, bacteria and other contaminants directly into the patient's body, with potentially fatal results. Hence, drug manufacturers also need to ensure that they keep up to date with any possible contaminants – such as HIV, hepatitis and bovine spongiform encephalopathy (BSE) in animal-derived biopharmaceuticals. More prosaically, the syringe-filling area requires a higher degree of cleanliness than, for example, the warehouse used to store the final packets.

## Premises and equipment

The design of premises and equipment intended for drug manufacture is critical to ensure the product's high quality. Thus the factory needs to be designed and operated in a way that avoids contamination and confusion between products. For example, raw materials and the finished product need to be separated and stored in clearly demarcated areas.

This can mean going to considerable lengths. For instance, many pharmaceuticals are manufactured in 'clean rooms'. This illustrates the extent to which drug companies may need to go in order to meet the authorities' requirements. Clean rooms use high-efficiency particulate air filters (HEPA filters) to remove particles and potential contaminants from the room's air supply. The air is pumped in through the filter then exits at floor level.

Regulatory authorities distinguish between several grades of clean air facility. In class A facilities, filters can occupy the entire ceiling – and these require regular cleaning and decontamination. Even 'lower' levels of clean air may still require filters that occupy a quarter of the ceiling space. Moreover, work surfaces and machinery must be designed in such a way as to avoid retaining dirt and microbes. Finally, personnel may need to enter through airlocks and wear sterile gowns, and processes are, as far as possible, automated. This almost eliminates particulate matter and microorganisms – whether pathogenic or not – from the environment, as Table 6.1 shows.

### Table 6.1: Definitions of clean air in pharmaceutical manufacturing

| European classification | Viable micro-organisms/m³ | Maximum permitted no. particles/m³ | | Equivalent FDA classification |
| --- | --- | --- | --- | --- |
| | | 0.5 µm particles | 5.0 µm particles | |
| A | < 1 | 3,500 | 0 | 100 |
| B | 5 | 3,500 | 0 | |
| C | 100 | 350,000 | 2,000 | 10,000 |
| D | 500 | 500,000 | 20,000 | 100,000 |

FDA = Food and Drug Administration

Source: based on Walsh, 1998, p. 82

## Documentation

As mentioned above, a company's manufacturing division must not only follow the rigours of GMP and its product licence commitments, it needs to be able to show that it has. This means that manufacturers must adequately document every stage of the process. Adequate documentation also (Walsh, 1998, p. 91):

- Helps prevent the errors and misunderstandings that can arise through verbal communication

- Helps the company to trace a particular batch's manufacturing history – this might be important if a product is recalled (see below) or found to be contaminated

- Helps ensure that the manufacturing process is reproducible – this guarantees a consistent product throughout the life cycle.

To achieve this, manufacturers use four main types of documentation (Walsh, 1998, pp. 92–93):

- *Standard operation procedures.* These offer detailed descriptions of how staff should perform a particular procedure or use a specific piece of equipment. Generally, standard operation procedures describe a procedure step by step and may cover, for instance, using a tablet-making machine, cleaning a work surface or sampling raw material. Standard operation procedures are regularly revised and review dates are laid down in the document. This ensures that, even if there are no changes, the standard operation procedure is regularly reviewed.

- *Specifications.* The quality control department formulates specifications based on, for instance, the pharmacopoeia or the product licence. Specifications detail requirements for raw materials and finished product, for example, along with the limits of tolerance. The specification may thus set out the percentage of active ingredient and the allowable levels of contaminants that pose no hazard to human health.

- *Manufacturing formulae, processing and packaging instructions.* Manufacturing formulae should clearly state the generic and product name, potency and strength as well as the batch size. The processing information is, in some ways, an extensive standard operation procedure covering the entire manufacturing process. Thus the processing information should cover the equipment used and the location in which each task is performed. The processing information also covers any important health and safety issues – some pharmaceuticals are highly toxic in their unformulated state and, for example, should not be handled by women of childbearing potential. Others may be potentially carcinogenic. Packaging instructions include the labelling of drugs as well as shipping and distribution. (Wholesalers and companies should follow Good Distribution Practice.)

- *Records.* As we have mentioned several times, maintaining adequate, detailed, validated records is a cornerstone of GMP. These records cover every aspect of the drug's manufacture, such as the specifications, batch manufacturing, packaging records and quality control. The records are retained for months, sometimes years, after the product expires. Regulatory authorities expect to be able to examine the records for any given batch of drug.

## Labelling

For pharmaceuticals, labelling plays a more important role than simply making a product stand out on the shelves. Indeed, aesthetic considerations are among the least important aspects of pharmaceutical labelling, even for OTC medications. The labelling, which needs to be approved by the regulatory authorities, offers important information that helps clinicians and patients use the product safely and effectively. For example, the label tends to include:

- Generic (chemical) and brand name

- Dose or strength

- Dosing instructions
- Storage instructions, such as 'Keep refrigerated'
- Expiry date
- Manufacturer
- Batch number.

Increasing numbers of regulatory authorities require that patient information leaflets are included with the finished product. These should be written in a manner that means that most people, whatever their educational attainment, can understand the instructions. So, for example, the patient information leaflet may list side-effects with likely incidence. They should avoid excessive jargon and be well designed. From January 1999, European laws dictate that full information leaflets and labels must be supplied with all prescription medicines. These 'patient packs' contain information on, for example, safety and administration.

## Quality control

As the name suggests, quality control departments ensure that the final product meets or exceeds standards laid down in the product licence and various statutory instruments, such as the pharmacopoeia. So, for example, the quality control department may analyse samples taken from each batch of raw material to ensure that it meets the specification. The raw material can be used only after the quality control department approves the batch. The quality control department may also follow the drug through manufacturing, in some cases taking samples at critical stages. The department may also analyse the final product to ensure that it meets specification and to validate its effectiveness. The latter is especially appropriate if the drug is a biopharmaceutical (Walsh, 1998, p. 152). The quality control department is responsible for approving the product's release for distribution to doctors, hospitals and pharmacists.

## Complaints and product recall

If there is a manufacturing fault that emerges despite Quality Control's best efforts, the company must have procedures in place to rapidly recall any relevant batches of medicine. For example, a company may recall a product because a pharmacist or clinician contacts the manufacturer to raise concerns about contamination or a mix up about dosage strength. In other cases, the regulatory authority may demand that a product is recalled because its analysis has revealed something amiss or following a clinician's or pharmacist's warning. This underlines the importance of clearly labelling each box of drug with the batch number.

Clearly, however, some recalls may be more urgent than others. The US Food and Drug Administration (FDA), for example, divides product recalls into three classes:

- *Class I recall*: 'There is a reasonable probability that the use of or exposure to a violative product will cause serious adverse health consequences or death'

- *Class II recall*: The product 'may cause temporary or medically reversible adverse health consequences or where the probability of serious adverse health consequences is remote'

- *Class III recall*: Using the product 'is not likely to cause adverse health consequences'.

Other regulatory agencies worldwide work to similar hierarchies. In the UK, the Defective Medicines Report Centre (DMRC) receives and assesses complaints and reports. If the DMRC believes that there has been 'a serious quality failure' it will, after discussion with the company, issue a drug alert letter recalling the batch and notifying health authorities.

## The global base and rationalisation

Increasingly companies find that drug manufacturing is most cost-effective if production of tablets is consolidated in one factory, liquids in another and creams somewhere else (Shahi and Cunningham, 1999). Indeed, drug manufacturing is now a global business: the drugs destined for a particular market may be made on the other side of the world. Indeed, in the case of some biopharmaceuticals, there may be a single manufacturer covering the entire world. However, the company cannot allow its quest to save money to compromise quality. The increasingly global basis of pharmaceutical marketing means that local authorities need to scrutinise the quality of drugs manufactured abroad.

As a result, European agencies, the FDA and local authorities randomly check imported medicines to ensure that they meet agreed standards for purity, strength and packaging. Inspectors also check labels and look for signs of possible contamination, such as cracked vials and broken bottles. (Such rules do not generally apply to small quantities of a drug imported by a visitor for their personal medical use – up to 3 months' supply, for example.)

Moreover, the FDA and other authorities often visit manufacturing sites abroad to ensure that they reach adequate standards and many regulatory authorities work together. So, the FDA enters into 'memoranda of understanding' (MOUs) with other governments to ensure products meet US standards for quality. The MOUs also ensure that the product is tested and sampled in a specific way before leaving the manufacturing country. Similarly, the UK authorities issue export certificates to help satisfy the receiving country's import requirements. These indicate that statutory requirements have been met and that inspections have been carried out. For example, the export certificate confirms that a company's products are sold in the UK and manufactured in accordance with GMP. The World Health Organization also runs a certification scheme.

In conclusion, the manufacturing division is at least as important to a pharmaceutical company's overall success as the R&D and marketing departments – despite its somewhat lower profile. Moreover, the manufacturing division needs to work within regulatory boundaries that are as rigorous as those facing any of the other departments. In many ways, the manufacturing division is the company's powerhouse: if it fails to deliver, the company could lose millions in sales. Do not underestimate its importance in the company's overall success.

# Chapter 7: Launch and marketing

Once a company has spent millions of pounds, dollars or yen researching, developing and manufacturing a drug, it has only a few years to recoup its investment. Ensuring that the company makes an adequate return on its investment is the responsibility of the sales and marketing department. However, companies' promotional activities raise several issues that anyone in the pharmaceutical sector needs to appreciate. In many ways, Sales and Marketing is the pharmaceutical sector's public face and its activities reflect – for good or ill – on every part of the company.

## The product life cycle

A patent (see page 103) gives the company protection from anyone copying the drug for 20 years, from the time of filing. However, taking the drug through the animal and clinical trials programme may take a decade from filing the patent. As a result, a company may have only 10 years to ensure an adequate return on investment. Moreover, sales of a drug follow a well-established pattern – the so-called 'life cycle' (Figure 7.1). As you can see, it may take several years before the company builds up peak sales, which in some cases can come between 8 and 11 years after launch. Only 15 of the 250 drugs with sales in annual sales in excess of $150m attained their peak revenue within a year (James, 2000).

**Figure 7.1: A pharmaceutical product's life cycle**

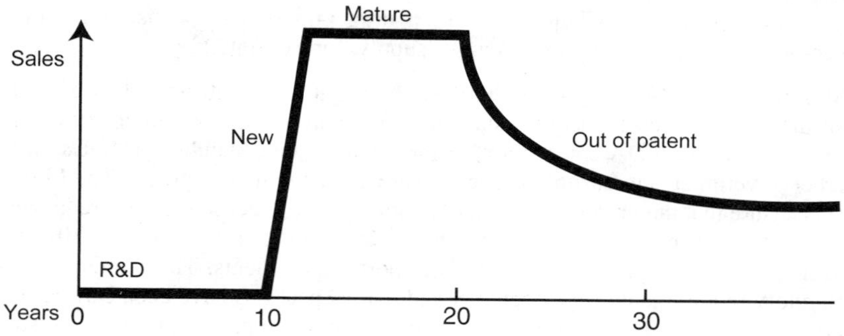

Source: ABPI

The product then enters a period of maturity. For a few years, the product sells, more-or-less, at its peak market share. The company makes most of its profits during this time. Finally, the product comes off patent and faces generic competition. Sales can then fall dramatically. Most companies use a variety of market indicators to track their sales performance and assess where they are in the life cycle. These are usually bought in from specialist companies, such as IMS.

Not surprisingly, companies aim to reduce, as far as possible, the time to peak sales and extend the mature phase. To achieve this, a new paradigm for life cycle management emerged in recent years. Traditionally, companies rolled out their international launches over several months: growing sales in one market helped fund the launch in another. According to the new model – used, for example, for Viagra (sildenafil) and Lipitor (atorvastatin) – the company combines simultaneous launch in several countries, improves sales force productivity, for example using IT, and employs direct-to-consumer advertising in the US. While this involves a greater up-front investment, the new model means that the mature phase is reached more rapidly (*PharmaBusiness*, 1999).

Companies can also take several steps to maintain sales once a product comes off patent – the tail of the life cycle. A company could, for example, enter an alliance with generic houses. It could make the product look unique – at its simplest by making the drug an unusual shape or colour. They could repackage in a calendar pack, for example.

A more sophisticated approach exploits the growing number of innovative drug delivery systems to either reduce side-effects or make dosing more straightforward. This may mean reformulating in a sustained-release formulation or considering radically different means of delivery – using an inhaler to deliver insulin or growth hormone, for example (page 74). In such cases, most of the value is in the patented delivery system rather than in the drug itself. As I noted in a recent report (Greener, 2000d): 'Reformulation may offer considerable perceived or actual added value. Thus, few companies can afford to ignore the impact of drug delivery on their own portfolios and on market dynamics.'

Building brand identity helps maintain sales against stiff genetic competition. Drugs such as Zantac and Prozac rely largely on their brand images to maintain their position in the wake of the launch of a growing number of rival brands in the same class or with the same indications, as well as several generics (*PharmaBusiness*, 1999). However, both Zantac and Prozac remain blockbusters (see Chapter 2), which partly reflects the success of their brand-branding strategy. Indeed, pharmaceutical advertising increasingly aims to build brand identity, both globally and within each market. The brand means that doctors buy more than the drug: they prescribe a set of values – such as higher quality and perception of a more reliable source. Advertising and marketing companies often use techniques derived from the promotion of fast-moving consumer goods – those goods that require constant replenishing, such as CDs and standard groceries – to build a pharmaceutical brand identity.

In general, these approaches – be it introducing a drug delivery system, investing in a brand or making the pill a unique shape – have the same aim. They aim to encourage customers to ask for a brand or to encourage the patient to pressurise the doctor to stick with the familiar formulation. Ideally, this should mean that the customer pays a premium for the brand. However, in pharmaceuticals, brands help protect against competition. Finally, the company could consider line extensions or explore new indications (see Chapter 5).

The growing importance of health technology assessment and health economics (see page 42) could also influence the life cycle. For example, companies have to engage with organisations, such as NICE, several years before a drug is launched. A positive recommendation could encourage more rapid uptake in the early phase of the life cycle and, perhaps, a higher plateau. On the other hand, if the assessment organisation requires further data – perhaps gathered from postlaunch studies – then uptake may be slower, although, if the outcome is favourable, the plateau could be higher. The impact of health technology assessment on the product life cycle is not yet clear. However, few people expect the impact to be negligible.

## Pricing

As mentioned in Chapter 3, pricing restrictions are the main way in which governments aim to control costs. To remind you: the US has a largely unfettered free market, although HMOs exert downward pressure on prices. Across most of the EU, government-appointed committees decide whether to approve the company's proposed price on the basis of a dossier of cost and benefits as well as domestic and international price comparisons. In the UK, the PPRS (see page 42) leaves the company free to price products at a level defined by the market, but sets a limit on profitability. Despite the differences, all governments increasingly compare local costs with those in similar countries. In response, pharmaceutical companies also look abroad to see what impact these variations could have on the price they attain. However, comparing pricing between countries is fraught with difficulties for both pharmaceutical companies and governments. For example, countries differ in macroeconomic policy, demographics, epidemiology and insurance schemes. As a result, setting a common price between countries is probably unrealistic (Danzon and Chao, 2000).

One analysis suggested that UK drug prices were 20% above the EC average, while US prices were 54% higher. In contrast, prices in France and Italy were, respectively, 30% and 28% lower. Other studies painted a similar picture. A US government estimate suggested that American prices were 32% higher than those in Canada (which regulates reimbursement less tightly than some EU member states) and 60% more than in the UK (Danzon and Chao, 2000). Meanwhile, a UK government analysis suggested that US prices were 88% higher than those paid by the NHS. As a recent *Financial Times* feature (Pilling, 2000) noted: 'The same pill made by the same company may cost half in Canada what it does in the US. In Mexico, it may cost still less.'

To examine the global variation in pricing in greater detail, health economists Patricia Danzon and Li-Wei Chao used indexes of manufacturer-level drug prices across all molecules in 1992, based on community sales in the UK, US, Canada, France, Germany, Italy and Japan. They then estimated the price per standard unit – a proxy for dose – relative to the US. On the basis of the quantities of drugs used in the US, the differentials were −16.6% in the UK, +2.1% in Canada, −32.2% in France, +24.7% in Germany, −12.9% in Italy and −11.6% in Japan. However, including the quantities used in each country, prices were consistently below those in the US, ranging from a 44% reduction in the UK to 67% in France. On the other hand, if the analysis employed the quantities used in the UK (which has the lowest *per capita* expenditure), all other countries show higher prices than those charged to the NHS (Danzon and Chao, 2000).

Danzon and Chao believe that the impact of weighting factors, such as the quantity of drug used, is 'an important finding.... It highlights the difficulty of making meaningful comparisons of pharmaceutical prices: patterns of medicine use vary so much from country to country.' They add that previous analyses that failed to account for the quantity of drug gave undue weight to high-priced products. 'Previous price comparisons have been seriously biased by the use of very small, unrepresentative samples, confined to leading branded products, excluding all generics,' they remark. Such methodological considerations may contribute to the difference in results between this and the other studies (Danzon and Chao, 2000).

However, while there clearly are international pricing differences, the authors note that: '[t]hese indexes show smaller cross-national differences in the average cost of drug therapy at manufacturer prices than implied by previous studies'. Nevertheless, the study confirms the widespread impression that countries with strict regulations 'appear to pay systematically lower prices' for global brands than those jurisdictions with fewer regulations: the US, UK, Canada and Germany. 'If, as seems plausible, broad global diffusion is an indicator of high therapeutic value, this suggests that regulation is biased against more valuable [innovative] products', they say (Danzon and Chao, 2000).

And there are other differences between the systems. In most countries, the launch price remains the same throughout the product life cycle. (Of course, inflation means that the cost declines in real terms.) This is not the case in Japan, where prices fall in real terms (Danzon and Chao, 2000). In Japan, real prices fall over the life course of the drug by 6.8% annually. (Prices also fall in Italy in real terms, by 4.3% annually.) Moreover, under the UK's PPRS (page 42), if the company exceeds its target, it can keep only up to 40% above the original permitted return. Anything over this must be repaid, e.g. by cutting prices.

The reason for the marked decline in pricing during the life cycle in Japan lies in its unique system. Medicines are a source of income for Japanese doctors. Fees paid to doctors under the national health insurance system for medical services and a fixed fee-for-service are insufficient to meet running costs. As a result, providers rely on discounts from the reimbursement price to make up the shortfall. The clinics retain the difference between the price they pay and the reimbursement price, known as the *yakkasa*, which accounts for 18% of the total drug bill. The *yakkasa* may be one reason why Japanese tend to use multiple medications and newer, higher-priced drugs (Macarthur, 1995). As a result, the drug price lists are revised every 2 years and, in general, prices are reduced to bring them in line with the average market price from the wholesalers. This reduces the life span of products and leads to a number of 'me toos' – drugs with little if any advantage over the original brands (Ono and Kodama, 2000). However, the price differences allow clinicians to continue to retain the *yakkasa*.

Partly because of these factors, prices may differ markedly between countries. However, not all pricing differences can be explained by such socio-economic factors. For example, according to a survey from Health Action International and Consumers International, the retail price of 15 of 18 dosage forms of 11 branded medicines is higher in some developing countries than in 10 Organisation of Economic Co-operation and Development (OECD) nations. And the difference can be marked. For example, the cost of diclofenac 50 mg, an NSAID, is 59 times higher in Argentina than in India (*Scrip*, 2000). Such differentials help encourage growing calls for differential pricing for the developing countries – AIDS treatments being the most high-profile example (see Chapter 10).

To complicate matters further, some parts of an individual market might be offered discounts – hospitals, for example. This was once common practice in the UK. The hospital-prescribed drug was seen as a loss leader in a chronic condition. All clinical considerations being equal, the hospital clinician would recommend the cheapest drug, small quantities of which were supplied by the hospital pharmacist. GPs would feel obliged to follow the consultant's recommendations, but the price to the community team was higher. This practice, understandably, causes considerable friction between the primary and secondary healthcare teams and may be on the way out. Nevertheless, similar discounting schemes for generics and other branded drugs remain commonplace. For example, discounts also help to ensure a drug's inclusion in the formularies of hospitals, primary care groups and managed care organisations.

## Marketing strategies

Discounting is one example of a marketing strategy employed by pharmaceutical companies. Traditionally, these marketing strategies are divided into two broad approaches:

- *Below-the-line* – advertising that does not entail paying commission to an advertising agency, including direct mail, exhibitions, point-of-sale material and free samples
- *Above-the-line* – mass media advertising, including press, television, radio and posters, on which commission is paid.

However, many advertising agencies are transforming themselves into communication companies, so the rule about commission does not apply. Nevertheless, the distinction between below- and above-the-line promotion remains a useful way to consider marketing strategies.

Advertising companies' transformation into broader communication agencies reflects changes in the marketplace. There is much talk of pharmaceutical marketing moving from the 'old game' of influencing only doctors through sales representatives' visits and advertising to a new game that engages the growing number of stakeholders in healthcare – managers, patients, nurses and other professions, as well as doctors – increasingly using new media. Few companies have fully embraced the new game – yet. So, while the balance between the new and old game is not clear, advertising and face-to-face promotion to clinicians will remain the cornerstone of pharmaceutical promotion for the next few years.

Certainly, the tried-and-tested traditional marketing of a medicine, which relies on persuading the doctor to prescribe the medication through a combination of sales representatives and advertising, can be effective. Advertising essentially aims to raise awareness of a product, summarise its benefits and persuade the doctor to prescribe. In particular, extensive advertising creates an air of confidence in the product. That is why you sometime hear advertising executives speak of AIDA: attention, interest, desire and action.

Sales representatives build on this with one-to-one contact with the doctor. This allows the doctor to examine and discuss the scientific data supporting any claim, which is usually summarised in a document called the 'detail aid'. As was discussed in Chapter 1, pharmaceutical companies make a considerable investment in sales representatives, who are generally well briefed in the clinical area as well as in the benefits and limitations of the drug they are promoting. In some cases, sales representatives detail a single product – this is especially true of hospital sales to specialists. However, primary care sales representatives often promote several drugs in order of commercial importance (defined by the sales targets each sales representatives aspires to). These are called the 'detail slots'.

Pharmaceutical sales representatives use variations on several key themes to influence doctors (Roughead *et al.*, 1998):

- *Reciprocation*: The sales representative offers samples, gifts, printed material, patient information leaflets or invitations to meetings or congresses. The latter may be held locally, nationally or internationally. However, hospitality during these meetings should be limited so that it is secondary to the scientific content. Funding meetings or supporting clinicians' attendance at a medical meeting offers the opportunity to meet local, national and international opinion leaders.

- *Appeals to authority figures*: The sales representative cites promotional claims supported by reference to professors or specialists. These are the opinion leaders carefully cultivated by pharmaceutical companies and public relations companies. Often opinion leaders are the lead authors in the critical phase III studies, for example. Opinion leaders are skilled at treading a fine line between independent scientific credibility and being regarded as unduly influenced by the pharmaceutical sector. As a result, most opinion leaders now disclose any financial support they have received from pharmaceutical companies, such as study grants, consultancy roles, speaking engagements, and so on. Many major medical journals now insist on such declarations before they publish the study.

- *Social validation*: Sales representatives refer to the peer group. If most of a doctor's colleagues are doing something, many physicians feel uncomfortable doing something different without good clinical reasons.

- *Direct request to use the product*: This can only work if the sales representative has already established a good working relationship with the doctor.

- *Debate*: Using questions or statements to move gradually from pre-agreed areas to a commitment to prescribe.

However, such tactics are open to abuse. There have been cases of meetings in exotic locations where the scientific content was limited to an hour or so in the evening. A combination of increased regulation and bad publicity stopped these flagrant abuses, which were in any case rare. Nevertheless, pharmaceutical companies' tactics still sometimes raise ethical concerns. The industry needs to be aware of these if it is to present itself appropriately.

For example, sales representatives often use drug samples. There is nothing wrong with this per se. However, in some cases, these drug samples are dispensed to a patient rather than the doctor's preferred choice, especially if the patient cannot afford a particular treatment. One paper (Chew *et al.*, 2000) asked physicians to report how they would act in three hypothetical situations. In some cases, the availability of drug samples would have led physicians to dispense and subsequently prescribe drugs that differed from their preferred choice.

Similarly, advertising raises several ethical concerns. Advertising is rife on the Internet, on satellite television channels and in the print media. But some doctors believe that advertising can lead to conflicts of interest. In a *few* cases in *some* non-peer-reviewed journals there is an explicit link between the editorial and advertising. For example, the company may agree to run an advert if the copy is favourable. More commonly, a public relations company may ghost-write an article for an opinion leader, who then reviews the feature and agrees to put his/her name to it. The advertising executive on the magazine will then try to persuade the company or media buyer – who purchases advertising on behalf of clients – to place an ad.

Despite appearances, this system rarely leads to direct conflicts of interest, especially in the main pharmaceutical markets and across the developed world. Doctors are a sophisticated, critical audience. Therefore, most magazines keep their advertising and editorial departments separate to limit any conflict. Moreover, opinion leaders would not keep their reputation for long if they agreed to flagrant advertising in a feature. And if all the magazine's copy were 'puff' then the publication would lose credibility and readers. Magazines and the public relations companies are all too aware of these concerns. As a result, most of the articles generated in this manner are as balanced and as scientifically rigorous as those directly commissioned by the magazine. Indeed, it is in everyone's interests to maintain independence between advertising and editorial.

Nevertheless, such concerns pervade even peer-review journals. One study looked at advertising revenue generated by medical journals in 1996. The estimated pharmaceutical advertising revenue ranged from $715,000 to $18,630,000. In five cases, the organisation that published the journal raised between 2% and 30% of its income from a single journal's pharmaceutical advertising. Four organisations raised at least as much from pharmaceutical advertising as from their membership fees. Glassman and colleagues (1999) concluded that: 'Potential financial conflicts of interest arising from pharmaceutical advertisements in medical journals may be substantial. The impact on professional societies' financial independence and behaviour is unknown.'

To me, the key phrases in this conclusion are '*may* be substantial' and 'The impact ... is *unknown*' (my italics). There is little firm evidence that advertising promotes conflicts of interest. The few cases where there seems to have been a conflict are rare. However, Glassman and colleagues show that the risk of conflict of interest remains a concern lingering in the back of the minds of many clinicians. Companies need to address such lingering concerns to maximise their promotional return. This means that both journals and the advertising need to ensure that they act and are seen to act ethically.

Nevertheless, there is no doubt that advertising can be effective. Wang and colleagues (1999) examined the impact of advertising on drug prescribing for hypertension (high blood pressure). Since the late 1980s, prescribing of calcium channel blockers and ACE inhibitors has increased, while use of the older beta-blockers and diuretics has declined. Wang *et al.* estimated the 'intensity of drug promotion' in four issues of the *New England Journal of Medicine* each year between 1985 and 1996. Advertising for calcium channel blockers increased from 4.6% of advertising pages in 1985 to 26.9% in 1996. Advertising for beta-blockers and diuretics declined to nothing by 1996 from 12.4% and 4.2% respectively. The increase in advertising of ACE inhibitors was less marked than for calcium channel blockers (3.5% against 4.3%). Although the total number of drug advertising pages per issue had decreased, the proportion devoted to calcium channel blockers nearly quadrupled. Wang and colleagues found that the increased promotion of calcium channel blockers paralleled the increase in prescribing. They conclude that '[a]n association between advertising and prescribing patterns could explain why [calcium channel blockers] have supplanted better-substantiated therapies for hypertension'.

Advertising is not the only factor in the marketing mix. So advertising alone is not the only factor underlying the increased sales of calcium channel blockers. But advertising may offer a surrogate for promotional spend generally. The key issue, of course, is that promotion may lead to the use of a less well-substantiated drug – which could cause toxicity or be ineffective. While this is not the case with calcium channel blockers, the paper illustrates another general concern among doctors.

Most doctors would counter that they take advertising with a large pinch of salt and that it has little impact on their prescribing habits. However, the figures seem to suggest otherwise.

## New approaches

As mentioned above, pharmaceutical marketing is becoming more sophisticated and increasingly engages doctors directly by offering value-added services. This began with the sponsored nurse, paid to perform a specific service or task such as running asthma or diabetes clinics. The company paid for the nurse, at least in the first few months, and expected to develop the market generally rather than directly encourage prescribing of a particular brand. (This would compromise the nurse's professional ethic.) Consider type 2 diabetes, which tends to emerge in middle age. Perhaps half of people with type 2 diabetes remain undiagnosed in some developed countries. Active screening and intervention by a trained nurse can detect and treat more cases. So, while the sponsoring companies rivals will gain sales, so will the sponsor.

More recently, purchasers and providers work alongside pharmaceutical companies to persuade doctors to implement a particular strategy. One recent UK initiative aimed to persuade GPs to switch to a cheaper proton pump inhibitor to release money to manage heart disease (Freemantle et al., 2000). Such collaborations are likely to increase in number, especially as many initiatives are educational rather than directly promotional. Indeed, in the UK, for example, the industry funds half of all GP further education and training. As medicine becomes increasingly complex, this trend will continue. Already, numerous specialised medical education companies specialise in doctor and nurse training.

Against this background, advertising and promotion is subjected to tight regulatory control. For example, the FDA oversees advertising and promotion in the US. However, some commentators are cynical about how effective such controls are. Shapiro (1997), for example, suggests that manufacturers may regard fines for unacceptable promotional activities as a business cost. Moreover, the pharmaceutical sector has an understandable desire to be involved on the regulatory board. Shapiro argues that representatives from the drug industry and those people who receive financial support from pharmaceutical companies 'cannot be genuinely independent'. The new promotional strategies pose particular problems, especially as they trend a fine line between offering value-added services or education and promotion. However, Shapiro suggests that regulation by government agencies is the most effective way to counter any undue influence.

However, it is also important to recognise the value of self-regulation. Pharmaceutical companies – ever wary of their rivals gaining a competitive edge – are among the most vigorous complainants to the regulatory authorities about unacceptable promotional activities. Indeed, marketing and medical departments will often go through a rival company's advertising and promotion copy with a finer-toothed comb than that used by any clinician.

## Direct-to-consumer advertising

In most countries, the promotion of medicines is tightly regulated. Across the EU, for example, it is illegal to advertise prescription medications to the general public. Any promotion to the public needs to be factual and balanced – in other words, it needs to be educational rather than promotional. This avoids patient education initiatives from becoming direct-to-consumer advertising by the back door. However, there is also a growing consensus that direct-to-consumer advertising is now inevitable in the EU. As we will see later, there is a clear need for more patient education. The health services have neither the time nor the inclination to meet this need. Direct-to-consumer advertising may offer one way to bridge the educational gap.

On the other side of the Atlantic, direct-to-consumer advertising is legal. And it has been a promotional route companies have willingly embraced. In 2000, more than $2bn was spent on direct-to-consumer advertising for prescription drugs in the US and spending is rapidly growing. The spend in the first quarter of 2000 was up by 58% over the same period in 1999, for example.

However, the medical community is split over the benefits offered by direct-to-consumer. Advocates suggest that advertising to the public promotes competition, which helps keep healthcare costs down. Moreover, patients, physicians and pharmacists are better informed about medication. This allows patients to develop a better therapeutic relationship with their clinician. In turn, this should help to reduce the burden of illness by reducing the need for hospitalisation and help to improve compliance with medication (Sellars, 2000).

Its opponents counter that direct-to-consumer advertising fuels demand, which drives costs up. They believe that the quality of advertising is variable and that patients are not equipped to evaluate medical information. This may lead to inappropriate prescribing and patients pressurising physicians into prescribing a particular medication that may not be the most appropriate in their case (Sellars, 2000). Certainly, making a drug available more widely, supported by advertising, can encourage inappropriate use. For example, in September 1949, the US FDA approved unrestricted sales of antihistamines. They became the most advertised and fastest-selling patent medications – sales reached $100m a year in 1950. However, much of the use was inappropriate – using antihistamines to stop the common cold, for example (*Scientific American*, 2000). This suggests that any advertising campaign needs careful consideration and control.

On the other hand, no one would argue that there is a need to better inform patients. The main debate centres on the means rather than the objectives. Only a third of patients act on medical advice to a sufficient degree to benefit. A third follow the advice, but not enough for it to be effective. The other third do not act on the advice at all. For example, between 50% and 70% of medications are not taken as prescribed (Illman, 2000, p. 5). Poor compliance may mean that the patient is inadequately treated and suffers the serious consequences that the drug seeks to prevent. Thus, noncompliance with antihypertensives can lead to a stroke. Apart from placing a heavy strain on health services, poor compliance with chronic medication undermines pharmaceutical profitability.

On the other hand, the mass media is an effective way to reach the general public. A recent UK survey reviewed sources of health information (Table 7.1). GPs are the commonest source, although it is clear that mainstream media are also very influential (Illman, 2000, p. 26). However, the Internet means that people can access information from the other side of the world. Moreover, a growing number of magazines are imported into Europe. This suggests that some patients on this side of the Atlantic are already exposed to direct-to-consumer advertising. Furthermore, many lay magazines follow up medical stories published in the professional journals. These factors, backed by intense lobbying from the pharmaceutical sector, mean that it is probably only a matter of time before direct-to-consumer advertising is approved in the EU.

### Table 7.1: Important sources of patient information

| Source | % citing as important |
|---|---|
| GP | 48 |
| Magazines and newspapers | 16 |
| TV | 13 |
| Friends and relatives | 8 |
| Practice nurse, health visitor and midwives | 6 |
| Pharmacist | 6 |
| Leaflets in GP waiting room | 5 |
| Other heath professional | 5 |
| Radio | 3 |

Source ABPI; some patients cited more than one source

### The role of public relations

Public relations companies aim to influence prescribing decisions by informing healthcare professionals, patients' groups and government as well as by creating a receptive market. So public relation companies may highlight problems with current treatments. They may aim to raise awareness of a particular condition among the general public, perhaps by holding an awareness week or day. Indeed, there is now a health awareness week for at least one condition during almost every week of the year. There is a danger that this will devalue what was once a valuable way of raising the general public's awareness of a disease.

More commonly, raising awareness means engaging the specialist and lay press. Medical journalists may be sponsored to attend medical conferences or attend press conferences to discuss a particular issue. Moreover, public relations companies help with opinion-leader development by, for example, training them to act as advocates for a treatment as well as showing them how to deal with hostile questioning and present themselves effectively on radio and television. Public relations companies also act a source of information for journalists wanting to know more about a particular product or company.

Finally, public relations companies often help pharmaceutical companies with crisis management. So they might help their client develop strategies to deal with contamination of a batch of drug, deaths among people taking the brand or a negative scientific report. While such events are rare, most companies already have plans in place to deal with the problem.

## Parallel imports

However, parallel imports can lead the best-laid plans of marketers array by distorting the market. The European Economic Area Agreement allows parallel imports – in other words, a drug can be imported from any member of the community. As, in some cases, drugs are cheaper in another part of the community, parallel importing may undercut the version of the brand available in that country.

Parallel importers have not been slow to make the most of the commercial opportunity, noting that it can to help control costs. Norway, for example, allowed parallel imports in 1995. By 1999, 91% of pharmacies dispensed parallel-imported drugs. While they are cheaper, 50% of the pharmacists and 54% of the physicians believed that parallel-imported pharmaceuticals represented an increased medical risk for patients. Some 15% of doctors and pharmacy staff had knowledge of either incorrect treatment or adverse drug reactions arising from the use of parallel-imported drugs (Gundersen et al., 1999). Critics note, for example, that parallel importing may mean that the pack contains information in a foreign language. For a drug with serious side-effects, this can pose a major problem. There are few controls against inappropriate transport and, while products made in that country need to meet domestic labelling regulations, the import needs meet only those of the exporting country (Kryzywicki, 2000).

Nevertheless, parallel importing is lucrative. In Europe, for instance, the number of parallel importers is between three and four times the number of mainline supply chain dealers belonging to the major wholesalers. In the UK alone, the parallel import market is worth around £700m a year. However, many industry insiders believe this to be a considerable underestimate (Kryzywicki, 2000). Indeed, the ABPI suggests that more than one in eight UK prescriptions are now filled using parallel imports, which accounted for more than 10% of 1998 sales. Parallel importing remains a bone of contention between the pharmaceutical industry and the regulators.

# E-commerce

Inevitably, the growth of the Internet will alter marketing strategies. In some cases, this has already happened. Brands such as Fosamax, for osteoporosis, the hormone replacement treatment Evista, and Prozac – to name only three – have dedicated websites. Corporate websites offer information on products for patients and professionals. Moreover, many sites for doctors, such as the *British Medical Journal*'s site, now carry Internet advertising. In some cases, these link to the company's website or an 'virtual detail aid'.

And sales of pharmaceuticals on the Internet are growing rapidly. In 1997, institutional pharmacies dispensed some 35% of the drugs sold in the US. Most of this reflected sales of prescription medicines; retail pharmacists sold almost 90% of OTC drugs. But the market is changing. Sales by mail services and food stores grew by 30% between 1996 and 1997, for example. In contrast, sales by independent pharmacists and hospitals rose by only 8% and 7.9% respectively over the same time.

The Internet will undoubtedly promote a reconfiguration of the pharmaceutical marketplace, as the importance of online pharmacies increases. The total global value of prescription, OTC, nutraceutical and personal care products sold on line may reach $2.5bn by 2003 – a 10-fold increase over 2000. However, it is worth remembering that making predictions in such a new area is fraught with difficulty. But, while the exact figures may be debatable, the fact that online pharmacies will be increasingly important is beyond doubt. Table 7.2 shows the expected growth in e-commerce in various business sectors.

### Table 7.2: Usage of and growth in e-commerce

| Industry/sector | Current usage (% of total) | Planned usage (% of total) | Growth (%) |
|---|---|---|---|
| Consumer goods | 8.4 | 43.4 | 517 |
| Energy | 23.3 | 37.2 | 160 |
| Financial services | 12.1 | 54.3 | 449 |
| Pharmaceutical industry | 6.1 | 33.3 | 546 |
| Processing industry | 9.2 | 34.1 | 371 |
| Public sector | 20.4 | 38.8 | 190 |

Source: Deloitte & Touche Consulting/Die Pharmazeutische Industrie, March 1999

For instance, wholesalers can host Internet sites that mainly offer healthcare advice and hypertext links to shopping mall sites or mail order drugstores. More controversially, some sites offer an Internet consultation with a doctor, who dispenses prescription medicine, supplied to the patient by courier or post. The latter highlights some of the ethical issues surrounding the Internet, which also include the confidentiality of electronic medical records (Singer, 2000). Nevertheless, the growth in the Internet, both as an advertising and information medium as well as a directly sales route seems inexorable.

# Chapter 8: Regulation

The pharmaceutical sector is among the most tightly regulated of all industries, with the possible exception of the arms trade. Pharmaceutical companies work within worldwide free trade agreements – in common with all large companies. However, pharmaceutical companies also work within ethical restraints during R&D and are subject to rigorous inspections during manufacturing. Before the drug is licensed, the information and data supporting the product and its claims undergo an intensive regulatory review.

The regulation does not end when the drug reaches the market. The company's advertisements and promotional material are subjected to legal restrictions that go well beyond those regulating fast-moving consumer goods, for example. Moreover, the authorities actively encourage doctors and other health professionals to highlight their concerns over side-effects or promotion. This unique regulatory framework is, in part, a response to the pharmaceutical industry's unique status and its unique product. However, the regulations mean that if the pharmaceutical companies make a mistake the consequences can be commercially catastrophic.

## Regulatory approval processes

No drug is totally safe – even the humble aspirin can cause gastrointestinal bleeding, for example. Even those drugs sold OTC are potentially hazardous if misused (although the risk of serious side-effects is much lower than with a prescription medication). However, the drug's chemical composition is not the only factor that determines safety. The information provided to the doctor and patient is also influential. Moreover, there is tight control on supply. Doctors still have the final say in the patient's treatment.

As a result, governments worldwide now operate regulatory organisations to independently evaluate and approve a drug before it reaches the market. However, in most cases, it took an accident to change attitudes. In the US, for example, a mistake in the formulation of a children's syrup in the 1930s led to the FDA's product authorisation system under the federal Food, Drug and Cosmetics Act.

Japan started requiring medicinal products to be registered for sale in the 1950s (ICH website). However, it was the thalidomide tragedy that prompted most European countries to introduce marketing approval for pharmaceuticals. As you probably know, in the late 1950s thalidomide was sold as a sedative and a treatment for morning sickness. However, by the early 1960s it was clear that thalidomide had caused severe birth defects in over 10,000 babies whose mothers had taken the drug while pregnant. Ironically, thalidomide may be an effective treatment for a variety of conditions, including AIDS wasting syndrome. Close surveillance of the drug and, in particular, ensuring that women do not become pregnant while using it recently allowed thalidomide to be re-marketed, under tightly controlled specialist supervision (Timmermans and Leiter, 2000). The thalidomide story underlines the point that safety is relative. For someone dying from AIDS wasting syndrome, reproductive toxicity is less of a concern than it is for a pregnant women who feels a bit queasy in the mornings.

Nevertheless, the thalidomide disaster promoted stringent drug regulations across much of the developed world. For example, in 1963, the UK's Committee on Safety of Drugs was formed. Around the same time, most other countries introduced similar schemes. More recently, European schemes were brought together under the European Medicine Evaluation Agency (EMEA) and there is increasing harmonisation between the deliberations of authorities in different parts of the world. Increasing harmonisation reflects the fact that, despite their superficial differences, all major markets critically evaluate the pharmaceutical company's data to ensure the safety, quality and efficacy of a new drug. Moreover, in some cases, there is a fourth hurdle – pharmacoeconomics (see page 42) – and most systems have some way of assessing safety once a drug is on the market (see page 102).

Here, we will briefly look at the regulatory systems covering the US, Europe and Japan. While there are differences, the 'explicit policy' underlying the regulation of medicines 'is that a drug should be made freely available to patients unless a case can be made for its availability being restricted' – usually safety concerns (Bradley and Blenkinsopp, 1996).

## US registration procedures

The US Food and Drug Administration covers food and nutritional substances, medical devices, cosmetics and toiletries – even microwave ovens – as well as pharmaceuticals. The FDA also evaluates advertising and promotional claims relating to these products (see Walsh, 1998, pp. 61–73 for more details). To meet its brief, the FDA, which is part of the US Department of Health and Human Science, operates through four offices:

- The Office of Policy
- The Office of External Affairs
- The Office of Management and Systems
- The Office of Operations.

The last of these is the office most drug companies come into contact with. Five centres report into the office of operations:

- The Center for Drug Evaluation and Research (CDER)
- The Center for Biologics Evaluation and Research (CBER)
- The Center of Devices and Radiological Health (CDRH)
- The Center of Veterinary Medicine (CVM)
- The Center of Food Safety and Applied Nutrition (CFSAN).

So, for example, the Center for Biologics Evaluation and Research covers vaccines and viruses, blood and blood products, antiserum, toxins and antitoxins used clinically in humans. The Center for Drug Evaluation and Research covers drugs and other biopharmaceuticals. However, both aim to fulfil the FDA's objectives:

- *To evaluate preclinical data to decide if clinical trials can proceed.* This data forms the investigational new drug application (IND). If the FDA does not object, usually within 30 days, clinical trials can begin. The IND reviews the drug's potency, purity and safety in animal studies as well as including the protocol for the proposed trial and product brochures for distribution to the trialists. As a result, the IND can run to 15 volumes of 400 pages each.

- *To protect patients' interests and rights.* For example, the FDA ensures that companies follow the Helsinki Agreement in clinical studies.

- *To assess the preclinical data and clinical trial data to see if a drug, biopharmaceutical or device should be approved for general use.* The sponsoring company submits a large dossier known as a new drug application (NDA), which can run to between 200 and 300 volumes and contain some 120,000 pages. If the medicine comes under the CBER, the company submits a product licence application (PLA), which is broadly equivalent to a NDA. However, the company must also provide a ELA (establishment licence application) to ensure that the manufacturing site is adequate.

- *To oversee the manufacture of medicines* (see Chapter 6).

- *To ensure the safety of the US blood supply.*

However, the FDA is not just a passive organisation. It meets with the clinical trialists and the sponsoring company to ensure that the trial is progressing safely. For example, many companies meet with the FDA to discuss the phase III protocol, which as we have seen is the most time-consuming and costly stage of R&D. It is also the stage that will be most influential in determining whether the NDA is approved.

Once the NDA has been filed it is reviewed by a multidisciplinary expert panel – including people holding doctorates in chemistry, microbiology, pharmacology, and so on. The FDA may also consult a technical advisory committee as well as questioning the drug company. The review's supervisors then examine the reports and make a recommendation to the divisional director, who then accepts or rejects the application or asks for more work from the company. All this can take 2 years or more (although some drugs that meet pressing clinical needs are fast-tracked). About a quarter of NDAs are not approved.

## The European system

As with so much in Europe, drug approval treads a fine line between protecting national interests and encouraging free trade, transparency and harmonisation between the member countries. So, for example, the regulatory system reflects the political aims of developing a single market for pharmaceuticals throughout the EU. In other words, pharmaceuticals should be marketed with identical conditions of usage in Austria, Eire and the UK.

To achieve this, the EU set up the London-based EMEA, which started work on 1 January 1995. This has now largely supplanted the old process where a company had to submit a separate licence application to each country in which it wanted to market a drug. In 1996, for example, the EMEA issued 1,632 certificates for medicinal products. By 1998, this had increased to 9,300.

Against this background, there are two main regulatory routes (see Walsh, 1998, pp. 61–73 for more details). First, there is a centralised route in which applications for a licence are managed and overseen by the EMEA. However, the EMEA does not directly review dossiers for biotechnology products and new chemical entities (NCEs). A selected EU country performs the detailed review. On the basis of this review, the EMEA decides whether to recommend the drug for approval. This decision is taken by the committee for proprietary medicinal products (CPMP), which draws on the skills of 30 technical experts – two from each EU country. (There is also a management board, a committee for veterinary medicinal products and a permanent secretariat.) Two CPMP members act as rapporteurs and are responsible for getting the application assessed within the agreed 210 days (assuming that no further information is needed from the company). However, the EC then takes the final decision as to whether or not to approve the drug for marketing, within 90 days of receiving the CPMP's decision. The approval lasts 5 years, after which time it needs to be reviewed.

Second, there is a decentralised route in which the company applies to a country's regulatory authority. The authority has 210 days to assess the application. If approved, the other members of the EU should accept the decision within another 60 days. The EMEA mediates any disputes within another 30 days. The EC will consider the EMEA's report and take a final decision to resolve the dispute. The EC's decision is binding. In other words, both the centralised and decentralised route take 300 days.

While the EMEA seems to have been successful, there are calls for the European regulatory environment to be amended to promote generic competition (Kanavos and Mossialos, 1999). Moreover, several issues remain to be brought within a European-wide regulatory framework, including parallel trade, standardisation, the single market and the member states' role in determining pricing and reimbursement levels. These factors means that the average delays arising through a combination of registration, pricing and reimbursement to the launch of a new drug range from 7 months in Denmark to 2.8 years in Austria and Belgium (Table 8.1).

## Table 8.1: Average delays in the launch of new drugs

| Country | Resgistration (months) | Pricing (months) | Reimbursement (months) | Total delay Months | Total delay Years |
|---|---|---|---|---|---|
| Austria | 24 | 3 | 6 | 33 | 2.8 |
| Belgium | 21 | 3 | 10 | 34 | 2.8 |
| Denmark | 7 | – | – | 10 | 0.8 |
| France | 12 | 3 | 9 | 24 | 2.0 |
| Germany | 30 | – | – | 30 | 2.5 |
| Greece | 21 | 6 | 6 | 33 | 2.8 |
| Italy | 12 | 6 | 5 | 23 | 1.9 |
| Netherlands | 18 | 0 | 3 | 21 | 1.8 |
| Portugal | 42 | 3 | 9 | 54 | 4.5 |
| Spain | 21 | 3 | 1 | 25 | 2.1 |
| Sweden | 11 | 2 | – | 13 | 1.1 |
| UK | 14 | 1 | – | 15 | 1.3 |

Source: British Pharma Group/*Die Pharmazeutische Industrie*, June 1998

## The Japanese system

In Japan, the ministry of health and welfare has overall responsibility for pharmaceutical law. Within the ministry of health and welfare, the pharmaceutical affairs bureau examines new drug applications (see Walsh, 1998, pp. 61–73 for more details). Essentially, these applications fall into three main types:

- *Shonin* – approval to manufacture or import a drug
- *Kyoka* – a licence to market the drug
- An official price.

Approval takes around 18 months and the requirements are broadly similar to those of the FDA. A reviewer examines the application to ensure that it conforms to the guidelines. A subcommittee of specialists then examines it. Again, the company needs to show safety, quality and efficacy. Traditionally, Japanese authorities require at least some of the studies to be performed in Japan. While this requirement has been criticised for building a trade barrier, there are justifiable reasons behind it.

## Postmarketing regulation

Despite the best efforts of R&D, adverse drug reactions (ADRs) are common. For example:

- Side-effects result in 5% of hospital admissions
- Between 5% and 10% of hospital inpatients experience adverse drug reactions
- Around 0.1% of medical inpatients and 0.02% of surgical inpatients suffer a fatal adverse drug reaction (Arnold *et al.*, 2000).

And in the community many more patients experience drug side-effects that, in some cases, they simple endure. However, sometimes these side-effects may prompt the patient to stop taking the drug. Clearly, they can compromise compliance. The risk of side-effects is one factor driving R&D programmes (Chapter 4).

Many side-effects are rare – too uncommon to be detected with certainty during the phase III programme – and emerge only once a drug is marketed. This is especially true if the risk–benefit ratio presupposes a low side-effect incidence, such as a contraceptive or vaccine. For example, postmarketing surveillance data from Japan and the US reported an incidence of adverse events associated with inactivated mouse-brain-derived Japanese encephalitis vaccine of 2.8 per 100,000 doses in Japan and 15.0 per 100,000 doses in the US. The study suggested rates for systemic hypersensitivity reactions of 0.8 and 6.3 per 100,000 doses respectively. With such a low prevalence, postmarketing surveillance is the only way to accurately characterise such side-effects (Takahashi *et al.*, 2000). As a result, most regulatory authorities have a system to detect adverse drug reactions. These augment the phase IV and SAMM studies performed by the pharmaceutical companies. The box looks at the UK system, which is one of the best developed.

---

### Postmarketing surveillance in the UK

In the UK, the regulatory authority established an adverse drug reaction reporting system in 1964 after the thalidomide tragedy. Doctors, dentists, coroners and, since 1997, hospital pharmacists fill in a 'yellow card' if they suspect that the patient has suffered an adverse event. These healthcare professionals are asked to report all suspected reactions, however minor, to new medicine – marked with a black triangle in drug lists. They should also report serious suspected reactions to established medicines, even if the adverse event is well recognised or the cause-and-effect relationship is uncertain. The Committee on Safety of Medicines (CSM) evaluates these reports to see if a pattern emerges and to better assess the risk posed by recognised serious side-effects. Over the 36 years since the introduction of the yellow card system, more than 400,000 reports have been submitted to the CSM. And over the years a number of drugs gave been withdrawn from sale as a result. Many more have had their licence changed.

Researchers in the UK's Drug Safety Research Unit (DSRU) took postmarketing surveillance a stage further and developed prescription-event monitoring (PEM), a large-scale systematic postmarketing surveillance. The scheme identifies patients prescribed a particular drug. Each patient's general practitioner then receives a personalised follow-up questionnaire, usually on the first anniversary of the initial prescription. This asks for information, especially any 'events' since starting treatment (Rawson *et al.*, 1990; Andrew *et al.*, 1996). Again, the DSRU looks for patterns of adverse events that might alter the risk:benefit ratio. By 1998, DSRU had performed 65 PEM studies involving, on average, 10,979 patients (Mackay, 1998).

Prescription-event monitoring offers several advantages over spontaneous reporting schemes such as the yellow card system. Healthcare professionals are more likely to respond to a request for information than to spontaneously report a problem. PEM produces more accurate incidence rates and allows researchers to compare drugs. Moreover, PEM allows researchers to examine specific patient groups, such as pregnant women, children and the elderly (Mackay, 1998).

## The patent system

A patent is a contract with the state, in the form of a government representative (the patent office). This contract excludes people other than the inventors or the company for which they work from using the invention without the patentee's permission for 20 years from the time the patent is filed. In the case of pharmaceuticals, filing a patent usually occurs several years before the drug is launched. However, in return for this 'exclusivity period' the patentee must make details of the invention public. The patent system aims to bring new inventions into the public domain as well as to encourage innovation by guaranteeing the investor a return on investment. However, not everything is patentable. The idea must be novel, not obvious, and useful – 'have utility' in the jargon (Tribble, 1998).

Under the patent system, which is similar worldwide, the company files a patent application – the so-called 'pat pending' stage. The patent office ensures that the idea is novel, not obvious and useful. If so, it grants the patent. For conventional chemical drugs and most biotechnology products, the patent system has worked well – although there were always rumblings of discontent that the period of exclusivity was too short to ensure an adequate return on investment. However, a recent debate about gene patents has suggested some other limitations of the current approach.

Numerous patents have now been issued for gene sequences and their applications. These raise considerable moral and legal dilemmas. For example, some commentators believe that patenting gene sequences, even as part of a diagnostic system, violates the 'product of nature doctrine' that underpins the patent system. According to the product of nature doctrine, a patent cannot be issued for laws of nature, physical phenomena and abstract ideas. In the same way, the argument goes, a particular gene sequence at a particular location is a state of nature. Therefore, whatever the technological difficulties involved in characterising the gene, the sequence should not be patentable (Magnus, 1998). It is rather like being able to patent a star discovered by the Hubble space telescope. You cannot patent the star, but you can patent the technology used to discover it.

Some critics of the product of nature doctrine argue that it overly simplifies the relationship between genotype and phenotype. It is not the gene per se that a company should be able to patent – this has no utility. Rather they should be allowed to patent the relationship between the gene and the phenotype. This allows the company to patent a sequence, but only in conjunction with a product. In other words, a test for a sequence known as *apoE4/2* could lead to screens for Alzheimer's and heart disease – and each would be patentable (Magnus, 1998).

However, other critics of the product of nature doctrine argue that in the real commercial world these are little more than rarefied philosophical ponderings. In reality, if a company cannot patent a gene sequence it cannot protect its intellectual property and therefore will be less likely to recoup a return on its investment (Magnus, 1998). This may mean that important scientific advances will not be marketed, which will undermine human health and wellbeing.

These issues have not been fully resolved. However, the patent system is beginning to keep pace with biotechnological innovation. For example, under European law, the human body and its elements cannot be patented. So you can no more patent a sequence of nucleotides than you can patent an arm or a leg. However, you can patent genes or gene fragments isolated from the human body or produced during technological processes. If these fragments meets the utility requirement, the law regards them as biological inventions. As a result, the directive specifically states that the patent must describe the industrial application of the sequence (Tribble, 1998).

However, the competitive biotech market means that some researchers are forced to file for patent when they might, in less competitive circumstances, have allowed unrestricted use of their discovery. Merck & Co., for example, took a strategic decision to patent certain genomic tools and assays they invented to allow their continued use. But the company offers nonexclusive use free to academics and to other companies 'at reasonable terms'. Merck & Co. should be praised for adopting this position. However, not everyone takes this ethical high ground. There have been cases of inventors restricting access to tools that would help to advance biomedical science (Tribble, 1998).

The problem with patenting shows that the regulatory frameworks often struggle to keep pace with market and scientific advances. For example, it is not clear whether the growing number of skin substitutes – used to treat ulcers and burns – are devices, dressings or pharmaceuticals. Indeed, even the definition of 'medicine' is under constant review. As mentioned above, the 'explicit policy' underlying the regulation of medicines 'is that a drug should be made freely available to patients unless a case can be made for its availability being restricted' (Bradley and Blenkinsopp, 1996).

Against this background, in March 2000 the UK's Medicines Control Agency (MCA) redefined what constitutes a medicine. Before then, a medicine came under the MCA's remit only if the company clamed or implied that it had a medicinal use – in other words, that the product treated or prevented a disease or condition. The new law covers medicines by function – in other words, a medicine is a substance that has a significant physiological effect. This could bring many herbs that were previously exempt from regulatory control – including St John's wort, valerian and *Echinacea* – under the MCA's jurisdiction. The move reflects some doctors' concerns about the hazards associated with some herbal remedies. At the time of writing, however, the implications of this were unclear (Ottaway, 2000).

# Transnational organisations

Finally, we will briefly look at some of the transnational organisations that influence the pharmaceutical sector. There are several bodies with special interests – such as global networks of industry associations and patient groups. Here, however, we will focus on the transnational organisations that aim to improve transparency and harmonisation between states. Some of these organisations set the political context for free trade generally and have implications for any company in any sector that wants to trade globally. These organisations are influential. The International Monetary Fund was established in 1944 in the wake of the hyperinflation, economic depression and fluctuating exchange rates, still fresh in the memory, that had contributed to the Second World War. The IMF – part of the United Nations – aims to stabilise exchange rates and facilitate international trade. Indeed, the IMF has become a major international influence – although it has always attracted controversy. For instance, the IMF help to restructure the debt of developing countries in the 1980s, aided the transition of formerly communist countries to a market economy in the early 1990s and helped resolve financial crises in Mexico and Asia in the mid- to late 1990s (Lastra, 2000). Another well-known and influential transnational organisation, the International Bank for Reconstruction and Development (IBRD) – the World Bank – is another part of the UN that finances development in member countries by lending to governments.

## The International Conference of Harmonisation

Some of these transnational organisations have a more direct influence on the pharmaceutical sector. For years, researchers have complained that studies performed in America were not admissible in Europe or Japan and vice versa. There are legitimate concerns about how different populations metabolise and react to drugs. However, in broad terms, good science in Tokyo should be good science in Toronto and in Turin. As a result, the regulatory requirements should also be broadly similar. The International Conference of Harmonisation (ICH) aims, as its name suggests, to encourage transparency between regulatory requirements across countries.

The first plans for the IHD emerged during the WHO International Conference of Drug Regulatory Authorities (ICDRA), which approached the IFPMA to develop a joint regulatory–industry initiative on international harmonisation. This led to the ICH, which was launched in April 1990. 'The International Conference on Harmonisation of Technical Requirements for Registration of Pharmaceuticals for Human Use' – to give ICH its full title – brings together the regulatory authorities of Europe, Japan and the US, as well as representatives from the pharmaceutical industry, to discuss scientific and technical aspects of product registration (ICH website).

In essence, the ICH aims to harmonise technical guidelines and requirements for product registration to reduce the need to duplicate the testing of new medicines during R&D. This should allow a more economical use of human, animal and material resources as well as eliminating unnecessary delays in global development and availability of new medicines, while ensuring drugs remain of high quality, safe and effective (ICH website). For example, the conference published the GCP and GMP guidelines commonly used worldwide. The ICH is just over a decade old. However, it has already transformed international regulatory relations.

## The European Union

Trade tensions contributed to both the First and Second World Wars. As a result, there was a determination among European leaders that such tensions should not arise again. This principle underpins the European Union. Initially, European countries co-operated politically and economically as the European Coal and Steel Community, founded in 1952. Five years later, this developed into the European Economic Community (EEC or Common Market) covering six member counties: Belgium, France, West Germany, Italy, Luxembourg and the Netherlands.

The EEC grew rapidly into the EU. The UK, Denmark and Eire joined in 1973, followed by Greece in 1981, Spain and Portugal in 1986 and Austria, Finland and Sweden in 1995. However, the EU is set to grow again: several ex-communist countries – the Czech Republic, Hungary, Poland, Romania, Bulgaria, Slovakia, Estonia and Latvia – have either entered into association agreements (which provide for free trade within 10 years) or have applied for membership. As membership expands eastwards, the EU remains true to several aims:

- To expand trade
- To reduce competition
- To abolish restrictive trading
- To encourage the free movement of capital and labour
- To establish a closer union among European people.

For pharmaceutical companies, the biggest impact of the free market in pharmaceuticals has been the consolidation of national regulations under the EMEA, transparency between countries' regulatory authorities, and parallel importing. However, free trade remains an ideal that the EU aspires to rather than one it has attained. As Table 8.2 shows, numerous factors distort the pharmaceutical free market across Europe. Most countries still have a considerable way to go before they attain a free market.

### Table 8.2: Pharmaceutical market distortion within the free trade European Union in 1998

| Control | A | B | Dk | Fi | Fr | Ge | Gr | Ir | It | Lu | Nl | P | Sp | Sw | UK |
|---|---|---|---|---|---|---|---|---|---|---|---|---|---|---|---|
| Price control | X | X |  | X | X |  | X | X | X | X | X | X | X |  |  |
| Price control | X | X |  | X | X |  | X | X | X | X | X | X | X |  |  |
| Average price |  |  |  |  |  |  |  |  | X |  |  | X |  |  |  |
| External reference price |  |  |  |  |  |  | X | X |  | X | X | X | X |  |  |
| Profit control | X |  |  |  |  |  |  |  | X |  |  |  |  |  | X |
| Internal reference price |  | X |  | X |  |  |  |  | X |  |  | X |  |  |  |
| Negative list |  |  |  |  |  | X |  | X | X |  |  | X |  |  | X |
| Price freezing |  |  |  |  |  |  | X |  |  |  |  |  |  |  | X |
| Price cuts |  |  |  |  |  |  |  |  |  |  | X |  | X |  | X |
| 'Cost' pricing | X |  |  |  |  | X |  |  |  |  |  |  |  |  |  |
| Listing |  | X |  |  | X |  | X |  |  |  | X |  |  |  | X |
| GP budgets |  |  |  |  |  | X |  |  | X |  | X |  |  |  | X |
| Expenditure ceiling |  |  |  |  |  |  |  |  | X |  |  | X |  |  |  |
| Generic promotion |  | X |  |  | X |  | X |  |  |  | X |  |  |  |  |
| Pharmacoeconomics |  | X |  | X |  |  |  |  | X |  | X |  |  | X | X |
| Price/volume contracts | X |  |  | X |  |  |  |  |  |  |  |  |  |  |  |

Source: EC Third Round Table 'Completing the Single Pharmaceutical Market'

## The WTO and Gatt

Finally, it is worth mentioning the two worldwide trade agreements that influence the general business environment for global pharmaceutical companies: Gatt and the WTO agreements. Briefly, the General Agreement on Tariffs and Trade (Gatt), first signed in 1947, aims to provide an international forum to encourage free trade between member states. Gatt aims to regulate and reduce tariffs on traded goods as well as offering a means to resolving trade disputes. Gatt now covers more than 110 countries.

The World Trade Organization (WTO), founded in 1995 after the Uruguay Round negotiations (1986–94), is a global organisation that regulates trade between nations. At its heart are the WTO agreements, negotiated and signed by the bulk of the world's trading nations and ratified in their parliaments. Some 138 countries are members.

Gatt and the WTO set the international trading context within which the pharmaceutical sector works. As Gray remarks (1999, p. 18) transnational organisations, such as Gatt and WTO, aim to 'project free markets into the economic life of every society'. They achieve this by compelling adherence to rules that release markets from being embedded in local socio-economic circumstances. While this does break down barriers to free trade between countries, and is a more civilised way to settle trade disputes than turning to the bullet or the bomb, a perceived lack of democratic accountability is leading to protests at most of the meetings.

# Chapter 9: What makes a company successful?

From the discussion so far, it should be clear that there is no universal way to build a successful pharmaceutical company. However, it is also true that the success of the big pharmaceutical companies relies largely on the sales of a few blockbusting drugs that came from the endeavours of a relatively small number of creative innovators – such as Paul Janssen, James Black and Gerhard Domagk (the latter's pioneering research led to the sulphonamides). It seems that the pharmaceutical sector is built on narrow foundations. And there are signs that the next generation of researchers isn't coming up with sufficient blockbusters to maintain the growth of large pharmaceutical companies as their current major selling brands come off patent.

To sustain average growth rates, a company needs to launch one product with sales of around £300m per year for each 1–1.5% of the world market that the company has. Overall, the pharmaceutical industry needs between 70 and 100 new products a year of this size to maintain its growth. Nevertheless, the number of new chemical entities that reached the market has declined sharply since the 1960s, when the global pharmaceutical industry introduced between 80 and 100 drugs a year. This fell to between 50 and 60 in the early 1980s and declined further to between 30 and 40 in the late 1990s (Horrobin, 2000).

And as mentioned before, the failure of large pharmaceutical companies to innovate at the required rate has helped to fuel the recent spate of mega-mergers. Publicly, the partners in the mega-mergers suggest that joining together increases R&D productivity, partly by streamlining process and making savings in, for instance, distribution, where there is usually considerable overlap between the companies. However, rather than merger mania primarily reflecting the need to invest and streamline R&D, the mergers may have occurred *because* large companies failed to innovate at the required rate. As we have also mentioned, while this buys companies time, whether the pipelines are sufficiently full to meet stock markets' demands for growth is something of an open question. Ironically, as companies become larger, their internal R&D productivity may decline. For example, Horrobin (2000) estimates that the number of internally generated drugs as a proportion of marketed chemicals has declined from 80% in the 1960s to 50% today.

On the other hand, smaller companies, whose management structures are more likely to foster creativity, may be able to meet the innovation deficit. Already, up to half a large company's marketed drugs may already be licensed or bought in. The ability of small companies to innovate reflects some fundamental differences between the larger pharmaceutical companies and their smaller partners. In particular, smaller companies are less likely to rely on market research to help determine their R&D priorities. If companies had listened in the 1960 and 1970s to market researchers, many of the blockbusters that drive current success would never have made it to market, including the PPIs, beta-blockers and cyclosporin (Greener, 2000e).

For example, companies aim to maximise the return on each R&D dollar they invest. So they do not invest in R&D if market research suggests that sales will not reach at least £300m a year. And they look to their market research departments to predict those markets likely to prove the most lucrative. Yet, market research's track record in predicting lucrative markets is not that impressive. If market researchers had been listened to, beta-blockers, $H_2$ antagonists and SSRIs would not have made it out of the lab and into the market (Horrobin, 2000). Similarly, the development of cyclosporin was almost stopped following marketers' sales estimates that were less than 10% of the final market share (Drews, 1999). In many cases, marketers are unable to predict the growth in medical technology – such as surgeons' growing success in transplanting organs other than the kidney – or the expansion of a drug into areas that, on the surface, are not related but that share similar pathologies. For example, organ rejection, rheumatoid arthritis and atopic dermatitis share some immunological characteristics that make cyclosporin and other immunosuppressants an effective and appropriate treatment. Researchers are often aware of such synergies. Market research is unlikely to detect the potential offered by these new indications.

Losec offers perhaps the most striking example of this. Initially, market researchers believed that omeprazole (Losec) could achieve peak sales of less than £1m – after all, antacids were widely used. The market was too small for Losec to be successful. Indeed, in 1970 the Astra board terminated the programme that developed omeprazole. However, Swedish government grants helped to fund continued development. In 1980, Abbott Laboratories pulled out of a co-development arrangement, believing that Losec's sales would not surpass $15m annually. During the 1990s, US sales alone reached more than $2bn annually (Horrobin, 2000). The problem is that market researchers may identify only what they are already aware of.

## Enhancing creativity

To be fair, the large companies are aware of the need to develop and foster creativity. As mentioned in Chapter 4, the key to a company's growth is to foster creativity – which is something the startup companies achieve well. However, large-scale changes take time to instigate. In the meantime, an active policy of mergers and alliances should help drive growth (see below). Culturally, the smaller companies offer the freedom for innovative researchers to work creatively and attract people who are ill-suited to the highly managed R&D environment that exists in today's large companies (Horrobin, 2000).

Certainly, corporate culture needs to change to maximise the opportunities to enhance creativity. In an interview for *PharmacoEconomics & Outcomes News* (Greener, 2000f) Dr Horrobin commented that senior management often does not realise that creativity is not a team effort. 'We need to identify brilliant individuals and give them a broad remit to do what they want,' he said. And sometimes that sometime means allowing researchers to make mistakes – something many companies, with one eye on their bottom line, appear reluctant to do.

Indeed, Dr Horrobin argues that going down blind alleys is 'a necessary cost of research … the company has to accept that most research fails'. Indeed, over-planning can limit diversity and, ironically, increase the risk of failure. As Drews (1999) also notes, the culture that led to Janssen, Domagk and Black was 'unplanned – could not have been planned. They did not arise from any entrepreneurial or strategic concepts and had nothing whatsoever to do with company politics.'

Nevertheless, large companies are beginning to take steps to enhance their creativity and responsiveness. It will take several years before a large company can change its internal structures to improve productivity. For example, there is a trend towards flatter corporate structures, which allow a company to be more responsive to changes in the marketplace as well as cutting down on the number of layers that a person needs to go through in order to have a decision taken.

## Knowledge management systems

To further enhance creativity, many companies are investing in knowledge management systems. These are, essentially, means of storing, retrieving and analysing knowledge. You may be familiar with the bibliographical databases, such as *Chemical Abstracts* and *Biological Abstracts*, published by the American Chemical Society since 1907 and BIOSIS since 1926 respectively. These grow at around half a million records each year (Kanehisa, 2000, pp. 25–26), reflecting the rapid increase in scientific knowledge. They began as printed books. However, they form the progenitor of today's computerised knowledge management systems.

Since 1965, the Chemical Abstracts Service has published the *CAS Registry*, which contains chemical substances linked by a unique number. Again, this is growing rapidly – at more than a million records a year. The *CAS Registry* number allows the user to link a number of different resources (Kanehisa, 2000, pp 25–26), another essential element of knowledge management systems.

The Medline online database, founded in 1971 and now freely available, and its hard copy counterpart, *Index Medicus*, have helped generations of researchers to find the papers they need for their research. Run by the National Library of Medicine in the US, Medline's ability to aid molecular biology received a boost in 1988 when it joined with the National Center for Biotechnological Information (NCBI). Medline is now linked with databases of DNA sequences, protein structures, 3D structures and so on. It also offers links to many publishers providing on-line journals (Kanehisa, 2000, pp. 25–26).

Many companies now use similar internal systems to integrate bibliographical data – which includes SOPs and internal reports – with their databases of chemicals and drugs. This can offer a rich resource. For example, Pfizer's drug library includes approximately 2,000,000 compounds and at the time of writing the pipeline holds more than 130 potential new treatments. This can provide some useful leads. As one commentator noted: 'The explosion of scientific knowledge means that there are many more areas where unpredictable advances are now possible' (Mulgan, 1996).

Knowledge management means more than simply storing information in databases. The systems can help define areas in which 'unpredictable advances' may be possible. Many knowledge systems can also compute new knowledge using a series of rules – such as those for deductive logic: if A, then B, for example (Kanehisa, 2000, p. 44). By bringing together disparate pieces of information, knowledge management systems can open new areas for the company to explore.

Finally, increasing globalisation helps drive the growth of knowledge management systems. Foreign-based subsidiaries increasingly generate, use and disseminate knowledge. Moreover, foreign affiliates can access external, novel knowledge sources. As a result, companies need to develop systems to generate, circulate and use knowledge (Zanfei, 2000) within a global industry.

However, in the final analysis, knowledge management systems, however technologically sophisticated, are really only tools. Their effectiveness depends on the creativity and skill of the person using the system. As a result, companies large and small need to foster the management systems that encourage innovation and creativity.

## The biotech problem

However, biotech companies have problems commercialising their innovations without the help of large companies. A recent report (Kettler and Casper, 2000) noted that, from the eight leading biotech companies involved in therapeutics, only 24 drugs have reached the market. However, as Tables 9.1 and 9.2 show, the pipelines appear full. There are also a number of other biotechnology companies that focus on developing platform technologies and diagnostics rather than therapeutics. This represents a lower-risk strategy than developing new medicines.

### Table 9.1: Leading public biotechnology therapeutic and hybrid companies' marketed medicines and products in development 2000

| Company | No. marketed medicines | No. products in development |
|---|---|---|
| Amgen | 3 | 11 |
| Biogen | 4 | 10 |
| Celltech | 1 | 20 |
| Chiron | 6 | 18 |
| Genetech | 8 | 17 |
| Medimmune | 2 | 6 |
| Oxford GlycoSciences | 0 | 1 |
| PowerJect | 0 | 4 |

Source: Kettler and Casper, 2000

### Table 9.2: Products in development in the pipelines of European public biotechnology companies 1999

| Country | Preclinical | Phase I | Phase II | Phase III |
|---|---|---|---|---|
| UK | 29 | 28 | 38 | 11 |
| Germany | 2 | – | – | – |
| France | 4 | 5 | 4 | – |
| Sweden | 5 | 7 | 2 | – |
| Denmark | 5 | 1 | 6 | – |
| Netherlands | – | 1 | 1 | – |
| **Total** | **45** | **42** | **49** | **11** |

Source: Kettler and Casper, 2000

The UK biotechnology business is the most advanced in Europe – more than 80% of UK biopharmaceutical companies have existed for more than 6 years. Moreover, while the 43 UK publicly listed biotech companies have some 75 medicines in development, the sector has so far produced only one marketed product. Moreover, none of the companies has yet turned a profit. The report suggests that institutional and regulatory reforms may be required to allow the sector to flourish (Kettler and Casper, 2000). In the meantime, large pharmaceutical companies are also heavily involved in biotechnology, as Table 9.3 indicates. Moreover, many more companies enter into alliances with smaller biotechnology companies.

### Table 9.3: Ranking of patentees by number of biotechnology patents and products

| Rank | Company | No. of patents | Major affiliates and products |
|---|---|---|---|
| 1 | Human Genome Sciences | 144 | SmithKline Beecham |
| 2 | Rhône-Poulenc Rorer | 140 | Pasteur Mérieux, Transgene |
| 3 | SmithKline Beecham | 132 | |
| 4 | University of California | 131 | |
| 5 | US Government | 119 | |
| 6 | Novartis | 100 | Genetic Therapy |
| 7 | American Home Products | 88 | Immunex, Genetics Institute |
| 8 | Novo Nordisk | 81 | |
| 9 | Chiron | 64 | |
| 10 | Merck & Co. | 56 | |

Source: Inframonitor/Financial Times Pharmaceuticals

## Alliances: bridging the innovation gap

As discussed above, over the short term, alliances with smaller companies, despite their small research budgets, may help large pharmaceutical companies make up the innovation deficit. Indeed, most large companies now have numerous alliances, ranging from comarketing and copromotion deals through equity share to product and technology transfer. However, R&D and marketing alliances are by far the most important, accounting for 63% of more than 800 deals.

Indeed, such alliances are an increasingly important part of most companies' strategies. Between 1993 and 1997, SmithKline Beecham forged more than 40 alliances. Both Bristol-Myers Squibb and Roche had over 35 over the same time. Of the top drug companies, Bayer and Takeda Chemical were the least enthusiastic at forging alliances. Nevertheless, they still managed around 10 alliances each in 1993–97. Moreover, each year Johnson & Johnson alone enters into more than 100 third-party transactions that include licensing arrangements and research collaborations.

Moreover, there are also research collaborations with centres of excellence. And many of these centres of excellence are showing increasing commercial acumen. Imperial College, London, typifies the this spirit. Between 1997 and 2000,

Imperial College established around one new company a month, about equally divided between the biomedical sciences and the physical sciences with engineering. Overall, according to the ABPI, the UK industry has provided £100m to academia. The progenitors of many of the blockbusters of tomorrow are being investigated in academic laboratories worldwide.

## Switching to over-the-counter drugs

As mentioned in the discussion of the life cycle (page 86), developing OTC formulations can be an effective way of extending the life of a drug, despite the fact that profitability in the OTC market is historically lower than in the prescription business. Nevertheless, the OTC market is large and growing (as Table 9.4 shows, from a UK perspective) and, as the profit and loss model shows (Table 9.5), companies can still expect a 27% operating profit.

### Table 9.4: The growth in the UK's over-the-counter market

| Year | Sales (£m) |
| --- | --- |
| 1960 | 33 |
| 1970 | 65 |
| 1980 | 246 |
| 1985 | 451 |
| 1990 | 855 |
| 1995 | 1,256 |
| 1997 | 1,296 |

Source: ABPI

### Table 9.5: Over-the-counter model profit and loss profile

| | Percentage of selling price |
| --- | --- |
| Sales | 100 |
| Cost of goods | 25 |
| Gross margin | 75 |
| Distribution | 3 |
| Sales force | 15 |
| Advertising and promotion | 25 |
| Marketing and administration | 5 |
| Operating profit (before general overheads, research and development and tax) | 27 |

Source: Fenwick Associates

As you might expect, companies who want to launch an OTC medicine need to meet several criteria set by the regulatory authorities. For example, the EU sets criteria for classifying medicines as prescription-only that include:

- Likely to directly or indirectly pose a danger to human health when used incorrectly or without medical supervision

- Frequently used incorrectly

- Contain substances with activity or side-effects requiring further investigation

- Normally prescribed for parenteral administration.

If a drug does not meet these criteria, the company can apply for sale of the drug to be allowed over the counter. To ensure safety, the formulations, dosages and indications may differ from those approved for prescription sale (Bradley and Blenkinsopp, 1996). Nevertheless, the markets vary widely. Italian OTC sales represent just 14.2% of the total 1997 market compared to 24.6% and 33.7% in France and Germany respectively (Minghetti *et al.*, 2000b).

Moreover, despite regulatory harmonisation, the legal status of drugs differs. For example, ranitidine remains prescription-only in Belgium, Ireland, Italy and Portugal but is sold over the counter in the other countries of the EU. Similarly, astemizole, carbocysteine, domperidone and nystatin remain prescription-only in the UK but all are sold over the counter in Eire and Belgium (Minghetti *et al.*, 2000b).

However, setting a realistic price may pose problems and lead to discrepancies between countries. For example, in countries with a system of fixed prescription price, the OTC medication should be priced at a similar level. In contrast, when many people are exempt from paying charges for prescriptions, they may be reluctant to purchase a switched product if a prescription alternative is available. Such factors influence companies' pricing policy towards their over-the-counter medications.

Despite this, there is an increasing trend towards OTC medication as companies try to extend their brands' profitable life. In the UK, more drugs switched from prescription-only medicines (POM) to pharmacy (P) medicines between 1994 and 1996 than over the previous decade. Furthermore, OTC drugs now include treatments – such as $H_2$ antagonists for indigestion – that are also sometimes used for serious, chronic conditions. The move has its critics. 'Some of the more recently deregulated medicines ... may not seem to doctors to be natural choices for over the counter use' (Bradley and Blenkinsopp, 1996).

Despite such concerns, the trend seems inexorable – especially as a larger number of OTC medicines allows patients to self-medicate and therefore reduces the demand on the healthcare system. Moreover, there are calls for certain drugs – such as beta-agonists, oral contraceptives and emergency contraception – to be available over the counter if pharmacists provide additional information (Bradley and Blenkinsopp, 1996). This reflects, again, the fact that drug safety is not a matter of the chemical's toxicological properties alone. The environment within which it is used and the information provided is also critical to ensure safety. However, if such moves are approved, a system will need to be in place to ensure adequate side-effects reporting. On the other hand, the growth of electronic information systems means that this should not present an insurmountable issue.

In response to these factors, many companies are boosting their presence in the OTC market. For example, Johnson & Johnson and Merck Consumer

Pharmaceuticals Co. formed a 50/50 joint venture in 1989 to develop and market a broad range of nonprescription products. In 1995, the company launched Pepcid AC over the counter, the first $H_2$ antagonist approved for direct sale to the general public.

## How a company develops

So how does a successful pharmaceutical company develop? It is worth looking at two companies that illustrate many of the themes that pervade this book: American Home Products and Johnson & Johnson.

The American Home Products Corporation was founded in 1926 and grew by turning 'little-known products and companies' into major products. For example, in 1943, American Home Products merged with Ayerst Laboratories, which was founded in 1925. Ayerst introduced Premarin (conjugated oestrogen tablets) in 1941. Premarin is now the most widely prescribed product in the US. (The cost means, however, that it does not generate the most sales.)

American Home Products' growth through mergers and acquisitions continued for the next 50 years. For example, in May 1998, Wyeth-Lederle Vaccines acquired Apollon, a leading biotech company specialising in DNA-based vaccine technology. As noted before, large companies need to obtain new intellectual input. One way to achieve this is to acquire biotech companies. Moreover, in 1998 American Home Products acquired the Solgar Vitamin and Herb Co., Inc., which extends its product range into nutriceuticals (pharmacologically active nutrients). Again, as mentioned before, this tactic offers companies a means to increase revenue by exploiting a related business area.

Johnson & Johnson's website shows that it followed a similar path of mergers, innovation and maximising the return on investment. In 1876, Robert Wood Johnson listened to a lecture by Sir Joseph Lister, the English surgeon who identified airborne germs as a source of infection during operations. For several years, Robert harboured the idea of a practical, commercial application of Lister's research: ready-made, ready-to-use surgical dressings. By the mid-1880s, the idea was marketed after Robert joined the partnership founded by his brothers, James Wood and Edward Mead Johnson.

Johnson & Johnson quickly spread worldwide – once again illustrating that globalisation is nothing new. The first Johnson & Johnson subsidiary opened in 1919 in Canada, followed by offices in the UK in 1924, Australia in 1931, Sweden in 1956, Japan in 1961, Greece in 1973, Korea in 1981 and Egypt in 1985. The trend continues today. In 1990, Johnson & Johnson opened offices in Moscow, Hungary, Poland and the former Yugoslavia. This was followed in 1991 by offices in the Czech Republic. More recently, Johnson & Johnson has entered the huge Chinese market (see page 123).

Johnson & Johnson grew rapidly. To prevent the corporate structure from becoming unwieldy, it organised its growing operations, which exploited the growing healthcare market, into the divisions or subsidiaries typical of many companies today:

- Surgikos, Inc., now Johnson & Johnson Medical, manufactured disposable surgical packs and gowns and now has a broad asepsis line

- Modess Division, today's Personal Products Company, produces sanitary towels

- Ortho Pharmaceutical Corporation began with a birth control product in the 1930s

- Ethicon, founded in 1941, manufactures surgical sutures and related ethical surgical products. In 1992, Ethicon split into two separate companies: Ethicon Endo-Surgery, which markets advanced surgical instruments for less invasive and traditional surgery, and Ethicon, which markets innovative products for wound management, soft tissue repair and women's health

- Ortho Biotech, formed in 1990, was the first biotechnology company developed and operated as a subsidiary of a major manufacturer.

Johnson & Johnson also actively acquired companies, such as McNeil Laboratories in 1959 and Janssen Pharmaceuticals in 1961. In 1977, McNeil became two companies: McNeil Pharmaceutical and McNeil Consumer Products Co., best known for its OTC painkillers. In 1993, Ortho-McNeil Pharmaceutical was formed from the merger of McNeil Pharmaceutical and Ortho Pharmaceutical. Mergers and acquisition remain a key strategy for Johnson & Johnson. From 1989–99, the company acquired 45 companies and product lines. During the same time, Johnson & Johnson divested 18 businesses that no longer fitted the company's long-term growth strategy.

## What makes a successful company?

So, what makes a successful company? It really comes down to three broad principles:

- *An ability to innovate*: R&D is the most obvious example of the key importance of innovation. But innovation is also essential in marketing, especially given the changing stakeholders and market dynamics. In manufacturing and distribution, innovative techniques can reduce costs. And in management, innovative approaches can help encourage creativity.

- *Maximise the return on investment*: Companies need to redefine the product life cycle by encouraging more rapid use in several markets rather than a slower rollout across the world. And they need to use OTC switching to extend the tail of the life cycle. Maximising the return on investment may also mean considering other synergistic areas: diagnostics and vitamins, for example. Companies also need to think globally – even if they are not global manufacturers, perhaps though alliances. Which brings us to the final key to success:

- *Actively consider mergers and alliances*: Medical science is now so complex, so diverse and changing so rapidly that no one person or company can master even a relatively small areas. As a result, many innovative ideas come from small, highly focused companies and academic departments. In some ways, big pharmaceutical companies are more adept at commercialising ideas than at generating the concepts themselves. So, alliances and licensing is perhaps the key to the sector's continuing success.

# Chapter 10: A glimpse of the future

As mentioned several times in the book, and as anyone who works for a drug company is all too aware, the pharmaceutical industry and the healthcare market are in transition. Mind you, they always have been. Change is just about the only certainty. However, the pace of change seems faster now than ever before.

For example, a growing desire by governments worldwide to hold down spiralling healthcare costs has been a fact of life for decades. Indeed, the issue of financing healthcare occupied the attention of the postwar government in the UK that established the National Health Service. There was, as Berridge (1999) notes, a perception that 'NHS costs seemed widely out of control'. This is not supported by the figures, but, in healthcare politics, perception is as important as the balance sheet. While the cost of healthcare has been an issue for more than half a century, increasing expenditure is beginning to raise real concerns about whether the healthcare expenditure of developed countries is sustainable. Pharmaceutical prescribing is easily definable and responds to pressure. So reducing pharmaceutical expenditure, whatever the arguments that increased drug expenditure would reduce costs, seems set to remain a political priority.

Moreover, over the next few years, the combination of technological and market trends will continue to force companies to re-evaluate their current marketing strategy, both strategically and in their R&D programmes. These are not revisited here. Rather, this chapter highlights some of the strategic trends that could become increasingly influential over the next few years.

## The pressure grows ...

Over the next few years, there is a danger that, without major structural changes in industry, the sector's growth may be below the double figures traditionally expected by stockbrokers and shareholders. On the other hand, the first years of the new millennium should also offer numerous opportunities for new therapies and developing existing and novel markets. Claims for the potential offered by the Human Genome Project are often overstated. Nevertheless, genomic research, augmented by high-throughput screening and other advances, offers the potential to yield millions of new targets. Unfortunately, drugs aiming at these targets will not become available in the short term. Yet, the stock market and shareholders often appear to be unwilling to wait. The trend towards mega-mergers is, in part, an attempt by the big companies to buy themselves time.

However, one unresolved issue reflects the size of the market. Most analysts assume that the broad dynamics will remain unchanged. But genomics could ultimately lead to the characterisation of hundreds or thousands of genetically determined 'subdiseases', each requiring a different, genome-based approach, such as a drug tailored to a particular metabolic pattern. And each of these approaches would need to be tested in clinical trials. However, many of the more targeted markets will be relatively small, perhaps with worldwide sales of less than £50m (Horrobin, 2000). How companies will resolve this dilemma remains a key issue.

There is also increasing pressure on prices. Worldwide pricing constraints mean that new drugs will need to be supported by watertight clinical and experimental evidence, which may mean more, rather than fewer, clinical trials. Moreover, increasing globalisation is beginning to erode pricing differentials, at least in the major markets – especially as health technology assessment organisations (of which NICE in the UK is the progenitor) are introduced worldwide (Backhouse and Mauskopf, 2000). Perhaps more tellingly, politicians are focusing increasing attention on international price comparisons. US senators recently raised the prospect that poor, uninsured elderly people might not be able to afford modern medicines. So they voted to allow the wholesale importation of cheap foreign drugs (Pilling, 2000). We have already seen the impact of parallel importing in the European Union. The effect on the world's largest free pharmaceutical market remains to be seen.

Moreover, today successive molecules tend to be cheaper than the first to market. In contrast, during the 1970s and 1980s, many second-to-market drugs were more expensive than the lead compound. In 1993, the Boston Consulting Group found that the later entrants were an average 14% lower in price than the market leader. In crowded therapy areas, the difference may reach 30%. A more recent analysis estimates that, overall, the price is discounted by 3% for each month by which the successive molecules trail the first entrant. With the exception of a 'small positive differential' in the UK, this impact is the same across most major markets. The relatively small impact, compared to generic substitution, reflects the fact that the subsequent drugs to market may offer real therapeutic benefits (Danzon and Chao, 2000).

As pressure on healthcare budgets worldwide will continue to increase, generic prescribing is likely to remain a mainstay of governmental attempts to contain costs. However, many companies will try to limit their exposure to generics. For example, some may reduce the cost of the brand to a level similar to the generic. This allows prescribers to offer the quality of the brand at the cost of the generic. Other companies will, either through alliances or acquisitions, allow generics to be marketed before the patent life expires. As the generic house often buys the drug from the originator and access to the generic market opens a supply chain for the brand, both benefit. As Table 10.1 shows, generic markets should be boosted over the next few years as major brands lose their patent protection. So most of the affected manufacturers are actively exploring new avenues to maintain their profitability.

## Will the trend towards mega-mergers continue?

Against this background, it seems that the trend for mega-mergers may not continue. The rate of mergers and acquisitions in the pharmaceutical sector increased by 800% between 1992 and 1997, compared to between 1980 and 1992 (Hess *et al.*, 1999). But, after all, there is a limit to just how large a company can become before the economies of scale in terms of marketing and production are outweighed by the problems of being too big to, for example, communicate effectively internally – even allowing for intranets and e-mail – or respond to changing market conditions. This is especially true of the pharmaceutical marketplace, which changes regularly and rapidly. Some commentators believe that this point may be rapidly approaching.

## Table 10.1: Patent status of the world's best selling medicines 1998

| Rank | World sales (£m) | Brand | Company | Generic name | Patent expiry |
|---|---|---|---|---|---|
| 1 | 2,686 | Losec | Astra | Omeprazole | 2002 |
| 2 | 1,784 | Zocor | Merck & Co. | Simvastatin | 2001–03 |
| 3 | 1,568 | Prozac | Eli Lilly | Fluoxetine | Expired |
| 4 | 1,412 | Norvasc | Pfizer | Amlodipine | 2003–04 |
| 5 | 1,167 | Lipitor | Warner-Lambert | Atorvastatin | 2010 |
| 6 | 1,081 | Renitec | Merck & Co. | Enalapril | Expired |
| 7 | 1,022 | Seroxat | SmithKline Beecham | Paroxetine | Expired |
| 8 | 1,010 | Zoloft | Pfizer | Sertraline | 2005 |
| 9 | 916 | Augmentin | SmithKline Beecham | Co-amoxiclav | Expired |
| 10 | 884 | Claritin | Schering-Plough | Loratadine | 2002 |

Source: ABPI Fact & Figures 2000/IMS

Nevertheless, the mega-mergers, as well as a number of smaller, less well-publicised mergers and acquisitions, have bought the companies time in the eyes of the shareholders and stock market while the products of R&D flow through the pipeline. But to date the mega-mergers and consolidations have made no difference in the marketplace or the lab (James, 2000).

Indeed, in a recent feature, pharmaceutical marketing consultant Barrie James (2000) describes the mega-merger strategy as being: 'akin to rearranging the deckchairs on the Titanic ... big pharma is fast running out of options'. James predicts that companies will construct alternative strategies. For example, he suggests that companies could develop 'highly focused disease, technology, customer and geographic franchises'. They will achieve this by continuing to build partnerships and alliances with competitors, suppliers, customers and so on. Indeed, some companies may even downsize or split into smaller units. The impact of genomics, which could lead to the fragmentation of the market into many smaller, less lucrative niches, may encourage this trend (Horrobin, 2000).

In the medium term, however, big pharmaceutical companies will remain a dominant force globally. Nevertheless, the number of smaller companies will continue to grow, especially as academics see startup companies as a means to exploit their intellectual property. So, for instance, some companies may focus on R&D, which they license to marketing and licensing experts. Other companies may diversify into becoming healthcare providers, especially by working with managed care systems worldwide. However, SmithKline Beecham recently sold Diversified Pharmaceutical Services, which suggests that the trend may not be universal. Nevertheless, other companies, as well as smaller niche players – working perhaps in cancer, diabetes, and some neurological disease – could offer broader healthcare provider solutions.

Ultimately, there could also be 'virtual' pharmaceutical companies that neither manufacture nor market drugs. These companies would provide only funding and managerial expertise. A virtual pharmaceutical company would outsource all stages of research, development, manufacturing and marketing.

Indeed, one of the two certainties is that there is unlikely to be a single panacea for the pharmaceutical industry's ills. The way in which companies will evolve depends on historical factors, their core competency and their funding base.

## Companies need to think globally

Apart from an ever-increasing rate of change, just about the only other certainty is that companies will need to think globally to ensure that they maximise their return on investment. At its simplest, this may mean licensing drugs to local companies. Nevertheless, the trend towards global brands, typified by Prozac and Viagra, seems inexorable. Moreover, increasing number of companies believe that they will improve the return on their investment by selling drugs in new markets rather than by licensing.

This is one reason why a growing number of Japanese companies are marketing drugs in Europe and the US rather than licensing out. Their growing presence on the world stage will help improve Japanese companies' position in the league over the next few years. Certainly, as mentioned in Chapter 1, Japanese pharmaceutical companies have traditionally punched below their weight on the world stage. As Kanba (1999) notes, 'As a knowledge-intensive industry that conserves resources, the pharmaceutical industry would appear to be well suited to the Japanese business environment'. A stronger global presence suggests that Japanese companies may soon make the most of their position.

However, globalisation brings in its wake a changing political and ethical environment within which pharmaceutical companies work. Anticapitalist riots in Seattle, Prague and London underline a growing unease, among some vocal and politically aware groups in society, about the impact and ethics of globalisation, especially given the lack of political accountability of many companies and pan-national organisations, such as the World Bank and the IMF (page 105). This political undercurrent could tarnish the pharmaceutical sector's public image.

For example, globalisation brings with it a new ethical focus. Traditionally, companies tend to view the world from the perspective of the major markets, the top 10 of which accounted for some 84% of the total global market in 1998. However, medical ethics, which covers the pharmaceutical sector's activities, can no longer be judged only from the perspective of the developed world. The new philosophical discipline of global bioethics aims to examine issues facing the world's population and identify solutions that transcend culture. As Singer, (2000) remarks 'Almost any debate in medical ethics today must give consideration to global implications' (Singer, 2000). The AIDS pandemic offers a striking example of this.

### The AIDS pandemic

It is debatable whether AIDS would have attracted research interest to the same extent if it had been a disease confined to the developing world. Nevertheless, the identification of AIDS, the isolation of HIV and the development of drug regimens that, while they don't cure AIDS, seem to significantly prolong life represents a triumph for academic and industrial researchers. Yet, despite the early fears, which helped to drive research, that AIDS would become a major pandemic in the developed world, it remains a condition that strikes with its greatest ferocity against societies least able to manage the disease.

Worldwide, some 5.4m people were newly infected with HIV in 1999. Moreover, around 34.3m people were HIV-positive and 2.8m people died from AIDS during 1999 (Soni, 2000). The problem is greatest in Africa. Some 4.2m people in South Africa – about 1 in 10 of the population – are HIV positive (Senior, 2000). Moreover, between a fifth and a quarter of the population of Zimbabwe has been estimated to carry HIV. But even this may be overoptimistic: screening of pregnant women suggests that almost 40% are HIV-positive. (Despite this, few people use condoms.) However, western drugs can cost some $10,000 a year – which countries such as Zimbabwe cannot afford (Ezzell, 2000). The expense of treatment means that patients tend to be treated only for opportunistic infections that arise later in the natural history of the disease (Senior, 2000). As a result, around 60% of infected people turn for help to traditional healers (Ezzell, 2000), whose treatments are at best ineffective and at worse dangerous.

Against this background, pressure has mounted over the last few years to make effective HIV treatments available to AIDS patients in the developing world. There was an accusation – either implicit or explicit – that drug companies were profiteering by keeping prices high so that only patients in the developed world could afford them. Of course, as we have seen, such arguments are over-simplistic. Companies need to recoup their R&D investment, for example, otherwise there would be far fewer new medicines. Nevertheless, there was a feeling that, as the developing world faced a humanitarian disaster, the companies had a moral responsibility to make treatment available. The sector's image, in the eyes of many, was tarnished – if not blackened.

Against this background, five leading manufacturers of AIDS medicines recently cut prices to increase access by sufferers in the developing world. For example, Glaxo Wellcome cut the price of its AIDS drugs by 85%. However, at around $2 a day, this is still more than the systems can afford. External funding is needed just to help seriously affected counties to meet the drugs bill. Moreover, many of these countries lack the infrastructure for prescribing antivirals.

Nevertheless, this represented a recognition that companies need to do more to make their products available to those in greatest need. And it raises the issue of differential pricing. As we have noted before, there is an increasing trend across much of the developed world towards price harmonisation. Yet AIDS opens the prospect of overtly pricing treatments according to ability to pay. Time will tell if this is a one-off or a trend.

It is a similar problem with vaccination programmes, which save almost 3m lives each year. However, between 3m and 4m children die each year from diseases that conventional vaccines could have prevented. Vaccines in development could save a further 8m lives a year (ABPI, 2000). Consider measles, for example. Across most of Europe, the incidence of measles is less than 1 per 100,000 of the population. In the developing world, measles claims more than 2,500 lives a day (ABPI, 2000). However, there have been notable successes. Vaccination has eradicated smallpox even in countries were the disease was once endemic (Rose, 1993, p. 127). Polio, once one of the most feared diseases, is also on the verge of being eradicated worldwide (ABPI, 2000). To help make the most of these advances, the WHO's Global Fund for Children's Vaccines will provide $150m in vaccines and funding in 13 developing countries between 2000 and 2005. The initial grants alone will save at least 100,000 lives.

However, with increasingly vocal groups calling for an end to debt in the developing world, increasing awareness of the plight of the developing nations and increasing appreciation of the socio-economic costs of disease (a healthy nation is less likely to go into debt), it seems set to become a trend. Indeed, the Pharmaceutical Research and Manufacturers of America highlights its commitment 'to working with governments and private-sector organisations to break down the barriers – physical, social, economic and political – that slow or prevent delivery of much-needed treatments'. Time will tell if these are more than fine words.

Certainly, a more fundamental problem may prove more difficult to resolve. The public and private sectors currently spend around $56bn on health research each year. However, the Global Forum for Health Research estimates that less than 10% of research funds are spent on the conditions that account for 90% of the global burden of disease. As a recent *British Medical Journal* editorial remarked, the figure 'is now widely quoted as epitomising the inequitable nature of health research'. For example, simple, low-cost technologies suitable for use in countries with few resources 'are undervalued and hence inadequately researched' (Lee and Mills, 2000).

Currently, funding for tropical medicines comes from governments, foundations – such as the Wellcome Trust and the Bill and Melinda Gates Foundation – and international agencies such as the World Health Organization (Lee and Mills, 2000). Pharmaceutical companies tend not to invest in tropical medicines because they are unlikely to recoup their investment. (Orphan drug programmes are based in the major markets.) Given the pressure on pharmaceutical companies to maximise their return on investment, this attitude is unlikely to change without a major change in shareholders' attitudes.

## Engage the public

The AIDS experience shows than the general public has considerable interest in science, particularly with respect to its impact on society. Moreover, tax revenues fund many academic institutes and eveyone eventually needs medicines. So you might expect companies and biomedical researchers to want to engage the general public in discussions – patients are after all the ultimate users of the fruits of their labours. Yet, researchers and companies rarely engage the broader stakeholders in discussions about, for example, ethics or the human impact of research projects. Indeed, when they do – over the thorny issue of animal experimentation, for example – researchers often seem defensive and ill at ease. As Harry Collins and Trevor Pinch note in their exploration of the relationship between science and society (Collins and Pinch, 1994, pp. 142–144): 'When something goes wrong with science, the scientific community reacts like a nest of ants with an intruder in their midst.'

However, Collins and Pinch (1994, pp. 142–144) also point out that science generally features increasingly on the political agenda. 'Citizens, when they vote, need to know enough to come to some decision about whether they prefer more coal mines or more nuclear power stations, more corn or cleaner rivers, more tortured animals or more healthy children, or whether these really are the choices.' Moreover, a *Nature* editorial noted that wider public discussion might help to prevent vested interests having a disproportionate influence (*Nature*, 2000). Many debates about bioethics seem to be won by those who shout the loudest rather than by those with the most persuasive argument.

On the other hand, scientists, medical professionals and pharmaceutical executives often suggest that the public is not able to properly evaluate complex scientific data. To a certain extent, this is a truism. But it also misses the point. The issue is not whether the public can understand the subtleties of the pharmacokinetic profile or the intricate details of a genetic polymorphism. They should understand what that *means* to them. For example, Archie Cochrane, who largely pioneered the use of randomised control trials, eventually took the view that any trial that was publicly acceptable was ethical (Rose, 1993, p. 107). It is difficult to see how as a society we can decide what is publicly acceptable without engaging the public in a debate.

In any case, the evidence does not support this nihilistic attitude. The US National Institutes of Health actively engages the general public in debates about the ethics of science and its human impact. They found that the general public has 'little difficulty' in understanding the aspects of science to a sufficient degree to take part in consensus conferences on, for example, ethics (*Nature*, 2000). Certainly, as a researcher who took up writing, I believe that most issues – however complex – can be explained to a reasonably well-educated general audience if you take the time and make the effort. Unfortunately, all too often it seems that scientists and the pharmaceutical industry are unwilling to do either.

Yet, this will need to change. Biomedical science increasingly treads into controversial areas – the use of fetal tissues, genomics, therapeutic cloning, and so on – that even academics cannot agree on the ethics of. Such issues are political and the debate needs to be engaged. Sadly, there is little sign of the biotechnology and pharmaceutical sectors wanting to lead that debate.

## Market trends

The increasing trend towards globalisation should also open some new markets. Over the short to medium term, the relative importance of the different markets will remain largely unchanged (Table 10.2). The overall world market is set to grow by 8% between 1998 and 2002, with total net sales increasing from $298.7bn to $405.9bn. However, the strongest growth is set to be in the Middle East and the Pacific rim. Africa and, to a lesser extent, Europe will show the lowest growth rates.

However, there could be one important exception: China could emerge as a major player. Under the 5-year plan from 2001–05, China plans to create 12 pharmaceutical companies that are large enough to rival current international players. Currently, there are some 6,300 drug companies in China. However, many are uncompetitive. Moreover, China recently established 200 biotechnology companies and has 140 development and production projects under way (*Marketletter*, 2000). Whether the Chinese will succeed in this ambitious project remains to be seen. Even if they do not, many western companies are expected to try to crack the world's largest population. For example, in 1990 Shanghai Johnson

**Table 10.2: Changes in the world pharmaceutical market 1998–2002**

| Region | Subregion | Share of world market 1999 (%) | Share of world market 2010 (%) | Growth rate 1998–2002 (%) |
|---|---|---|---|---|
| America | North America | – | – | 9.8 |
| | US | 32 | 35 | – |
| | Latin America/Caribbean | – | – | 8.4 |
| Asia | Japan | 20 | 15 | 4.9 |
| | South-east/China | – | – | 11.0 |
| | Australasia | – | – | 9.8 |
| Europe | | 33 | 30 | 5.8 |
| | Eastern Europe | – | – | 8.6 |
| Others | | 15 | 20 | – |
| | Middle East | – | – | 10.6 |
| | Indian subcontinent | – | – | 8.6 |
| | Africa | – | – | 3.3 |
| | Former Soviet Union | – | – | 6.7 |

Source: FT Pharmaceuticals, IMS Health

& Johnson Ltd, a joint venture producing Band-Aid adhesive bandages, was opened in China, followed the next year by Johnson & Johnson China Ltd. Many other leading companies have followed suit.

The increasing presence of western companies in China could lead to a large number of new leads for R&D. Traditional Chinese medicine is of proven effectiveness in several chronic diseases. Studies suggest that Chinese herbs are effective in, for example, diabetes (Vray and Attali, 1995) and diabetic kidney disease (Gao et al., 1998), atopic eczema (Xu et al., 1997) and dysmenorrhoea (Kotani et al., 1997). Indeed, ethanobiology is likely to become increasingly important as drug companies search for chemicals active against the targets revealed through genomics and high-throughput screening. Chinese traditional medicine could offer a rich harvest of potential lead compounds for R&D. Indeed, the earth is host to some 265,000 flowering plants. Less than 0.5% have been studied exhaustively for their chemical composition and possible medicinal value. Clearly, however, this means preserving the environment. Merck & Co has invested $1m to preserve an area of the Costa Rican rain forest (Cox and Balick, 1994).

# Disease trends

As pharmacology advances, healthcare professionals are increasingly able to treat diseases that once proved fatal or dramatically undermined quality of life. However, this means that other diseases can come to the fore. The eradication of bacterial infections as a common cause of mortality has contributed to the pre-eminence of heart disease in the developed world, for example.

Moreover, the growing number of elderly people in the population also alters the complexion of disease patterns. In the US, people over 65 years of age currently consume 30% of prescription medicines and 40% of OTC formulations, despite accounting for only 13% of the population. It is a similar picture in the UK, where elderly people consume 45% of medications but account for 18% of the population (Mintzer and Burns, 2000). According to the World Bank and the United Nations, 7.3% of the world's population will be over 65 years of age by 2010. This will increase further to 20% by 2030 (Gareri et al., 2000). Clearly, these demographic changes will drive demand for treatments for diseases of old age, such as some cancers, osteoporosis and dementia. Moreover, as age-related changes in pharmacokinetics and pharmacodynamics can complicate therapy (Gareri et al., 2000), clinical trials will need to account for these factors.

To illustrate these disease trends, we will briefly consider two areas. Firstly, sexual problems will, for example, become more common as the number of elderly people increases. A survey of 3,000 Americans found that 43% of women and 31% of men reported experiencing sexual problems. However, the problem is best characterised among men, where impotence increases with age. The increasing number of older people means that in 25 years' time, more than 330m men worldwide will suffer from at least mild or moderate impotence (Goldstein, 2000). Impotence offers just one example of an age-related disease that, as the elderly population increases and its advocacy groups become more vocal, will represent important areas of unmet clinical need.

Even today, diseases that become more common as the population ages – such as type 2 diabetes, benign prostatic hyperplasia and cancer – account for a considerable proportion of disease spend (Table 10.3). However, as Table 10.4 shows, age-related diseases such as arthritis, hearing impairment and prostate disease represent major illness burdens, which can only become heavier with the increasing number of elderly people in the major pharmaceutical markets. Table 10.5 offers a snapshot of the drug areas in development for elderly people.

Certainly, the pharmaceutical sector has not made the same inroads into deaths from these diseases as it has in other areas. For example, the death rate in England and Wales for prostate cancer was 16.9 per 100,000 of the population in 1971. In 1997 it reached 31.1 per 100,000. Of course, in part this reflects the fact that men are not dying of other diseases, as well as enhanced case finding. Nevertheless, it also shows the considerable unmet need arising from the diseases of old age.

### Table 10.3: US annual expenditure on disease treatment

| Disease | Expenditure ($bn) |
| --- | --- |
| Diabetes | 113 |
| Cardiovascular disease | 110 |
| Mental illness | 85 |
| Cancer | 35 |
| Asthma | 4.7 |
| Benign prostatic hyperplasia | 4 |
| Peptic ulcer disease | 3.7 |
| Other conditions | 944.6 |

Source: Lewis Group/Financial Times Pharmaceuticals

## Table 10.4: Major chronic conditions in the US

| Type of condition | No. illnesses/1,000 males ≥ 65 years | No. illnesses/1,000 females ≥ 65 years |
|---|---|---|
| Arthritis | 428 | 553 |
| Hearing impairment | 354 | 238 |
| Heart disease | 360 | 299 |
| High blood pressure | 319 | 395 |
| Ischaemic heart disease | 191 | 123 |
| Deformity or orthopaedic impairment | 153 | 174 |
| Cataracts | 129 | 192 |
| Diseases of prostate | 126 | |
| Chronic sinusitis | 116 | 175 |
| Tinnitus | 113 | 73 |
| Diabetes | 107 | 96 |

Source: Financial Times Pharmaceuticals

## Table 10.5: Number of drugs in development for age-related diseases

| Indication | No. drugs in development |
|---|---|
| Cancer | 350 |
| Heart disease and stroke | 'more than 100' |
| Respiratory and lung diseases | 28 |
| Alzheimer's disease | 26 |
| Depression | 26 |
| Diabetes | 25 |
| Parkinson's disease | 16 |
| Osteoporosis | 14 |
| Rheumatoid arthritis | 11 |
| Gastrointestinal disorders | 11 |
| Prostate disease | 9 |

Source: Pharmaceutical Research and Manufacturers of America

Secondly, obesity is now so common that it is replacing undernutrition and infection as the single biggest contributor to illness. For example, obesity contributes to diabetes, coronary heart disease, some cancers and disorders related to sleep-breathing problems, such as heart failure. Indeed, Kopelman (2000) notes that: '[o]besity should no longer be regarded simply as a cosmetic problem affecting certain individuals, but an epidemic that threatens global wellbeing'.

However, there is some debate about whether obesity is really a disease. Fat people certainly suffer from more diseases than their leaner counterparts. But is something that makes you ill a disease? As Rollin notes (1995): 'Boxing may lead to sinus problems and Parkinson's disease – that does not make it in itself a disease.' In other words, just because a physiological mechanism predisposes to an event or state that leads to disease, that event or state is not necessarily a disease. 'To define obesity as a disease is to presuppose a highly debatable valuational judgement,' Rollin writes (1995, pp. 44–45).

These are more than rarefied philosophical concerns – they cut to the heart of the lifestyle drug debate. If obesity – and the same applies to alcoholism and other addiction – are not diseases, does the health service have a duty to treat sufferers?

It seems to me, however, that this simply puts obesity, alcoholism and addictions in the same area as hypertension or raised lipids. We treat raised blood pressure and elevated cholesterol not because they are 'diseases' but rather to prevent a heart attack or stroke in the future. Moreover, dental caries is largely the result of eating refined, sugar-laden food. Water fluoridation reduces the prevalence of caries, even although sugar consumption remains high (Rose, 1993, p. 127). There is, therefore, no difference between water fluoridation for caries and, for example, using lipid lowerers to reduce cholesterol while people still eat a fat-rich diet. According to the same principle, we should treat obesity, alcoholism and addictions to prevent the physical consequences. This, to me, justifies the treatment of lifestyle conditions. (But it depends on the extent of the physical and psychological consequences. That is why not funding baldness treatments may be acceptable.)

Nevertheless, few would argue that the problem posed by obesity and its related disease is set to increase. US national survey data suggest that between 1976/80 and 1988/94 the prevalence of obesity (the percentage of the population who are affected at any one time) increased from 14.5% to 22.5%. The average body mass index rose over the same period. These trends show no sign of slowing down (Flegal and Troiano, 2000). Managing obesity will emerge as a key challenge facing the healthcare sector. Tackling obesity and many other diseases may means forging a new alliance between the industry, healthcare and other agencies.

In the population more generally, lifestyle drugs will become increasingly important. While such drugs attract considerable controversy, most health services have already established the principle of managing lifestyle diseases.

## A secure future

As disease becomes ever harder to mange, the future may lead to more sober expectations of what the pharmaceutical industry can deliver – especially as the advances heralded by the genomics revolution do not emerge over the short term. For a long time, clinicians and the general public seemed to believe that medical science and its handmaiden, the pharmaceutical industry, would soon find a pill for every ill. But, as Geoffrey Rose notes (Rose, 1993, p. 128), 'that optimism has passed (except in the popular media) and we are starting to sober up'.

Certainly, pharmaceuticals can cure many diseases and alleviate the symptoms of most others. However, the incidence of disease generally remains high. As we cure one disease, another takes its place. As a result, the pharmaceutical industry is likely to survive – although it might change its form.

That is not something you can predict with certainty for many other sectors. Aerospace might be replaced by different forms of transport, petrochemicals by different types of fuel, and so on. Perhaps banking is the only other sector with a secure future. Human society has long needed a means of exchange and they have always needed medicines. There is no reason why that will not continue. So there is no reason, despite its current difficulties, why the pharmaceutical industry should not survive and flourish in the 21st century and beyond.

Indeed, in some ways the pharmaceutical sector has yet to grow up. It was born only around 150 years ago. Today, it seems to be in its adolescence. It has grown rapidly and even – in the debates over animal experimentation, for example – seems somewhat sullen. But it will be interesting to see just how the sector grows up!

# Glossary and abbreviations

**Above-the-line**: Mass media advertising, including press, television, radio and posters on which commission is paid

**ABPI**: Association of the British Pharmaceutical Industry

**ACE**: Angiotensin converting enzyme

**Acetylcholine**: A neurotransmitter

**Acetylsalicylic acid**: Chemical name for aspirin

**ADME**: Absorption, distribution, metabolism and excretion – the phases of pharmacokinetics

**ADR**: Adverse drug reactions

**AIDS**: Acquired immune deficiency syndrome

**Alzheimer's disease**: A common form of dementia

**Aminotransaminase**: A liver enzyme

**APMA**: Australian Pharmaceutical Manufacturers Association

**Assets**: A tangible (e.g. a building) or intangible (e.g. knowledge) object of value to the company that can usually be turned into cash either directly or indirectly

**Atypical antipsychotics**: Drugs used to treat schizophrenia that do not cause sedation

**Below the line**: Advertising that does not entail commission to an advertising agency – including direct mail, exhibitions, point-of-sale material and free samples

**Bronchitis**: A lung infection

**Calcium channel blocker**: A type of drug (also called a calcium antagonist) used to lower blood pressure and treat angina

**Capital**: The total value of assets less liabilities

**Carcinogenic**: Linked to an increased risk of cancer

**CBER**: Center for Biologics Evaluation and Research

**CCB**: Calcium channel blocker

**CDER**: Center for Drug Evaluation and Research

**CDRH**: Center of Devices and Radiological Health

**Cerebrovascular disease**: The process that leads to stroke

**CFCs**: Chlorofluorocarbons, propellants used in, for example, asthma inhalers

**CFSAN**: Center of Food Safety and Applied Nutrition

**CGI**: Clinical global impression

**Chemotherapeutics**: Using chemicals rather than natural products to treat disease

**CPMP**: Committee for Proprietary Medicinal Products

**CRA**: Clinical Research Associate

**CROs**: Clinical Research Organisations

**CSM**: Committee on Safety of Medicines

**CVM**: Center of Veterinary Medicine

**Cytochrome p450**: A group of liver enzymes responsible for metabolising drugs and other chemicals

**Cytokines**: Proteins that carry messages between cells

**Dividend yield**: Dividend expressed as a percentage of the share value

**Dividend**: The proportion of earnings that a company pays its shareholders, usually expressed as earnings per share

**DMRC**: Defective Medicines Report Centre

**DNA**: Deoxyribonucleic acid

**Dose–response relationship**: The relationship between dose and the biological action – usually, increasing the dose increases the response up to a plateau

**Double blind study**: Neither the patient nor the doctor knows the drug's identity

**DSRU**: Drug Safety Research Unit

**DTC**: Direct-to-consumer

**Dyslipidaemias**: Dangerous levels of cholesterol and other lipids in the blood

**Dystonia**: Muscle weakness

**Earnings per share**: *See* Dividend

**EC**: European Commission

**EEC**: European Economic Community

**ELA**: Establishment licence application

**EMEA**: European Medicine Evaluation Agency

**Endometriosis**: A disease of women characterised by abnormal growth of uterine tissue

**Enzymes**: Biological catalysts that speed up reactions

**Equities**: The company's ordinary shares; if the company is liquidated, ordinary shareholders split the assets remaining after paying creditors according the number of shares each holds

**Equity**: The net value after the company's creditors have been paid off

**EU**: European Union

**Evidence based medicine**: The use of scientific studies, rather than experience and anecdote, to guide medical and surgical treatment

**Excipients**: Inactive ingredients used in pharmaceutical manufacture

**Fast-moving consumer goods**: Goods that require constant replenishing, such as CDs and standard groceries

**FDA**: Food and Drug Administration

**FTSE**: Financial Times Stock Exchange

**Functional genomics**: How a gene's products act

**Gatt**: General Agreement on Tariffs and Trade

**GCP**: Good Clinical Practice

**Generics**: Off-patent drugs that can be made by any appropriately licensed company

**Genomics**: The study of genes

**GMP**: Good Manufacturing Practice

**Gold standard**: The current best treatment

**GP**:  General practitioner

**Growth factors**:  Proteins that stimulate growth

**Growth inhibitory factors**:  Proteins that inhibit growth

*Helicobacter pylori*:  The bacterium that causes many gastrointestinal ulcers

**HEPA**:  High-efficiency particulate air filter

**HFA**:  Hydrofluoroalkane, a propellant used in, for example, asthma inhalers

**HIV**:  Human immunodeficiency virus

**HMO**:  Health maintenance organisations

**Hoehn and Yahr scale**:  A measure of the severity of Parkinson's disease

**Hydrophilic**:  Water attracts the molecule

**Hydrophobic**:  The molecule is repelled by water

**Hypertension**:  High blood pressure

**IBRD**:  International Bank for Reconstruction and Development

**ICDRA**:  International Conference of Drug Regulatory Authorities

**ICH**:  International Conference on Harmonisation

**IFPMA**:  The International Federation of Pharmaceutical Manufacturers Associations

**Immunosuppressant**:  A drug that suppresses the immune system – used in, for example, transplantation medicine, rheumatoid arthritis and atopic dermatitis (eczema)

**In vitro**:  Studies performed in the test-tube

**In vivo**:  Studies performed in animals or humans

**IND**:  Investigational new drug

**Intangible assets**:  Intellectual property, such as patents, copyrights and trademarks

**Intron**:  DNA and RNA that does not code for a gene

**IRB**:  Institutional Review Board

**Knockout mice**:  Mice bred without a particular gene to examine its effect

**LD$_{50}$**:  The dose of a drug that kills half of a group of animals

**Loan capital**:  The amount of money provided to the company through loans

**Macromolecules**:  Large molecules, in particular proteins and peptides

**Me-toos**:  Drugs developed to cash in on a market with little if any additional clinical benefit

**MOUs**:  Memoranda of understanding

**Muscarinic**:  A type of receptor that binds acetylcholine

**Nasdaq**:  National Association of Securities Dealers Automated Quotations

**NCE**:  New chemical entity

**NDA**:  New drug application

**Neuroleptics**:  Drugs used to treat schizophrenia that cause sedation

**Neuromodulators**:  Chemical transmitters that 'fine tune' the activities of nerves

**Neurotransmitter**:  A naturally produced chemical that carries messages between nerves

**NGOs**:  Nongovernmental organisation

**NHS**: National Health Service

**NICE**: National Institute for Clinical Excellence

**Nicotinic receptors**: A type of receptor that binds acetylcholine

**NSAID**: Nonsteroidal anti-inflammatory drug

**OECD**: Organisation for Economic Co-operation and Development

**Operating profit**: The company's profit (or loss) made from its main trade – calculated from operating expenses and trading profit before allowing for extraordinary items

**OTC**: Over-the-counter

**PEM**: Prescription-event monitoring

**PhRMA**: Pharmaceutical Research and Manufacturers of America

**PLA**: Product licence application

**Placebo**: An inactive drug used to measure the effectiveness of an active drug

**Pneumonia**: A lung infection

**Post-transcriptional modification**: Processing of the gene product

**PPI**: Proton pump inhibitor

**PPRS**: Pharmaceutical Price Regulation Scheme

**Premalignant**: Cellular changes likely to develop into cancer

**Proton pump inhibitor**: A type of drug used to treat gastric ulcers

**Purine**: A metabolic product that forms uric acid

**QALY**: Quality-adjusted life year

**Quinine**: A drug for malaria

**R&D**: Research and development

**Receptors**: Proteins that bind naturally produced transmitter and hormones as well as drugs

**Revenue**: *See* Sales

**RNA**: Ribonucleic acid

**Sales**: The value of the goods that the company has sold

**SAMM**: Safety assessment of marketed medicines

**Schizophrenia**: A mental illness characterised by hallucinations and a dissociation from reality

**Second messenger systems**: Intercellular pathways that switch the chemical process on and off

**Selective serotonin reuptake inhibitor**: A type of drug used to treat depression and other psychiatric conditions

**Share capital**: The amount of money provided to the company by selling shares

**Single blind study**: A study in which the patient is unaware of the identity of the treatment taken

**SMOs**: Site management organisations

**SOPs**: Standard operating procedures

**SSRI**: Selective serotonin reuptake inhibitor

**Tangible assets**: Land, buildings, plant and machinery, fixtures and fittings, trading stock, etc.

**Taxol**: A drug from the Pacific yew tree used to combat ovarian and metastatic breast cancer

**Theophylline**: A drug for asthma

**Trading profit**: The company's profit before deducting interest, directors' fees, auditors' remuneration, etc.

**Transgenic**: Genetically modified

**Turnover**: Total sales over a defined time – such as annually or quarterly

**Type 2 diabetes**: A type of diabetes that tends to emerge in middle age and does not normally require to be treated with insulin

**Viral load**: The number of viral particles in the blood

**WTO**: World Trade Organization

# References

4S (1994) Randomised trial of cholesterol lowering in 4444 patients with coronary heart disease: the Scandinavian Simvastatin Survival Study (4S). *Lancet* **344**, 1383–1689

ABPI (2000) *Prevention is better than cure: how vaccines contribute to health.* Association of the British Pharmaceutical Industry, London

Adams, J.C. (2000) *Shakespeare's physic*, Royal Society of Medicine, London

Addington, D. (1995) The use of placebos in clinical trials for acute schizophrenia. *Canadian Journal of Psychiatry* **40**, 171–176

Andrew, J.E., Prescott, P., Smith, T.M. *et al.* (1996) Testing for adverse reactions using prescription event monitoring. *Statistics in Medicine* **15**, 987–1002

Arnold, A., Welch, S. and Coultas, A. (2000) Development of an adverse drug reaction reporting scheme. *Hospital Pharmacist* **7**, 79–80

Ayres, J.G., Frost, C.D., Holmes, W.F. *et al.* (1998) Postmarketing surveillance study of a non-chlorofluorocarbon inhaler according to the safety assessment of marketed medicines guidelines. *British Medical Journal* **317**, 926–930

Backhouse, M.E. and Mauskopf, J.A. (2000) Formal requirements for economic analysis of medicines: the potential implication of the UK NICE requirements for global product development. *Decision Resources* **11 April**

Barnes, J. (2000) New Horizons in pharmacovigilance: DURG meeting highlights. *Inpharma* **1247**, 19–20

Berridge, V. (1999) *Health and society in Britain since 1939*, Cambridge University Press, Cambridge

Binder, M. and Nell, G. (1999) Oral terbinafine (Lamisil) in the short-term treatment of fungal infections of the skin: results of a post-marketing surveillance study. *Mycoses* **42**, 555–558

Bradley, C. and Blenkinsopp, A. (1996) Over the counter drugs: the future for self medication. *British Medical Journal* **312**, 835–837

Burstall, M.L. (1997) The management of the cost and utilisation of pharmaceuticals in the United Kingdom. *Health Policy* **41**(Suppl.), S27–S43

Calam, J. (1996) *Clinicians' guide to* Helicobacter pylori, Chapman & Hall, London

Cherry, S. (1996) *Medical services and the hospitals in Britain*, 1860–1939. Cambridge University Press, Cambridge

Chew, L.D., O'Young, T.S., Hazlet, T.K. *et al.* (2000) A physician survey of the effect of drug sample availability on physicians' behaviour. *Journal of General Internal Medicine* **15**, 478–483

Collins, H. and Pinch, T. (1994) *The golem: what everyone should know about science.* Cambridge University Press, Cambridge

Concato, J., Shah, N. and Horwitz, R.I. (2000) Randomized, controlled trials, observational studies, and the hierarchy of research designs. *New England Journal of Medicine* **342**, 1887–1892

Connee, E. (1999) Metaphysics and the morality of abortion. *Mind* **108**, 619–645

Cox, P.A. and Balick, M.J. (1994) The ethanobotanical approach to drug discovery. *Scientific American* **June**, 60–65

Danzon, P.M. and Chao, L.-W. (2000) *Prices, competition and regulation in pharmaceuticals: a cross-national comparison.* Office of Health Economics, London

Datson, L. (ed.) (2000) *Biographies of scientific objects.* University of Chicago Press, Chicago, IL

De Jonge, M.J., Loos, W.J., Gelderblom, H. *et al.* (2000) Phase I pharmacologic study of oral topotecan and intravenous cisplatin: sequence-dependent hematologic side effects. *Journal of Clinical Oncology* **18**, 2104–2115

Den Boer, J.A. (1997) Social phobia: epidemiology, recognition, and treatment. *British Medical Journal* **315**, 796–800

Dobbs, S.M., Dobbs, R.J., Weller, C. *et al.* (2000) Link between *Helicobacter pylori* infection and idiopathic parkinsonism. *Medical Hypotheses* **55**, 93–99

Drews, J. (1999) *In quest of tomorrow's medicines,* Springer, New York

Edgerton, D. (1996) *Science, technology and the 'British' industrial decline 1870–1970,* Cambridge University Press, Cambridge

Ezzell, C. (2000) Care for a dying continent. *Scientific American* **May**, 72–81

Flegal, K.M. and Troiano, R.P. (2000) Changes in the distribution of body mass index of adults and children in the US population. *International Journal of Obesity* **24**, 807–818

Freemantle, N., Johnson, R., Dennis, J. *et al.* (2000) Sleeping with the enemy? A randomised controlled trial of a collaborative health authority/industry intervention to influence prescribing practice. *British Journal of Clinical Pharmacology* **49**, 174–179

Galbraith, J.K. (1997) *The affluent society,* 4th edn, Penguin, Harmondsworth

Gao, Y., Lu, R., Wang, X. *et al.* (1998) A clinical trial of *tang shen ning* for treatment of diabetic nephropathy. *Journal of Traditional Chinese Medicine* **18**, 247–252

Gareri, P., Falconi, U., De Fazio, P. *et al.* (2000) Conventional and new antidepressant drugs in the elderly. *Progress in Neurobiology* **61**, 353–356

Gerbino, P.P. and Joseph, A.S. (1993) Multisource drugs: implications and concerns in the geriatric population. *Hospital Pharmacy* **28**, 96–98, 101–102

Gerdtham, U.G., Johannesson, M., Gunnarsson, B. *et al.* (1998) Price indices of drugs and the switching to new drugs. Two empirical examples. *Pharmacoeconomics* **13**, 71–80

Girard, P.M., Pegram, P.S., Diquet, B. *et al.* (2000) Phase II placebo-controlled trial of fozivudine tidoxil for HIV infection: pharmacokinetics, tolerability, and efficacy. *Journal of the Acquired Immune Deficiency Syndrome* **23**, 227–235

Glassman, P.A., Hunter-Hayes, J. and Nakamura, T. (1999) Pharmaceutical advertising revenue and physician organizations: how much is too much? *Western Journal of Medicine* **171**, 234–238

Goldstein, I. (2000) Male sexual circuitry. *Scientific American* **August**, 56–61

Grabowski, H.G. (1982) Public policy and pharmaceutical innovation. *Health Care Finance Review* **4**, 75–87

Gray, J. (1999) *False dawn: the delusions of global capitalism,* Granta Books, Cambridge

Greener, M. (2000a) From herbs to medicines: a new opportunity for the new millennium. *Nutraceuticals International* **Jan**, 16–17

Greener, M. (2000b) NICE's impact: you can run, but you can't hide. *PharmacoEconomics & Outcomes News* **278**: 3–4

Greener, M. (2000c) Counting the cost of Parkinson's disease. *Pharmaceutical Times* **July/August**, 12

Greener, M. (2000d) Leading applications of inhaled delivery systems for systemically active drugs. *Decision Resources* **27 Sept**

Greener, M. (2000e) R&D: it's not size that matters. *PharmacoEconomics & Outcomes News* **276**, 3–4

Greener, M. (2000f) New study challenges old international pricing certainties. *PharmacoEconomics & Outcomes News* **279**: 3–4

Gundersen, R., Torgauten, O. and Olsen, H. (1999) Pharmacists' and general practitioners' views on parallel import of drugs. *Tidsskrift de Norvegisk Laegeforeningen* **119**, 1586–1588

Hamada, T. (1996) Medical and pharmaceutical tales recorded in *Genroku-Sekenbanashi-Fubunshu. Nippon Ishigaku Zasshi* **42**, 563–580

Harvard (1991) *The race to develop human insulin*, Harvard Business School, Cambridge, MA, 9–191–121

Hattori, A. (1991) The way for carrying medicine and its containers (V). Packaging material – paper. *Yakushigaku Zasshi* **26**, 59–64.

Healy, D. (1997) *The antidepressant era*. Harvard University Press, Cambridge, MA

Hendricks, J.C., Sehgal, A. and Pack, A.I. (2000) The need for a simple animal model to understand sleep. *Progress in Neurobiology* **61**, 339–351

Hertzberg, R.P. and Pope, A.J. (2000) High-throughput screening: new technology for the 21st century. *Current Opinion in Chemical Biology* **4**, 445–451

Hess, G.P., Watrous, M.L., Stutton, D.R. *et al.* (1999) The role of pharmaco-economics in response to globalisation and increased competition in the pharmaceutical industry. In: *Pharmacoeconomics and outcome assessment: a global issue*, ed. S. Salek, Euromed Communications, Haslemere, Surrey, pp. 119–142

Holden, A. (1999) *William Shakespeare*, Little, Brown & Co., London

Horrobin, D.F. (2000) Innovation in the pharmaceutical industry. *Journal of the Royal Society of Medicine* **93**, 341–345

Illman, J. (2000) *The expert patient*, ABPI, London

Jackson, R. (1988) *Doctors and diseases in the Roman Empire*, British Museum Press, London

Jackson, W.A. (1996) *The Victorian chemist and druggist*, Shire Publications, Princes Risborough, Bucks

James, B.G. (2000) Is big pharma too tied to old business solutions? *Scrip Magazine* **September**, 7–9

Johannesson, M., Jonsson, B., Kjekshus, J. *et al.* (1997) Cost effectiveness of simvastatin treatment to lower cholesterol levels in patients with coronary heart disease. Scandinavian Simvastatin Survival Study Group. *New England Journal of Medicine* **336**, 332–336

Johnson, G. (1995) International relations. *Economics Medicines and Health* **Spring**, 28–30

Kanavos, P. and Mossialos, E. (1999) Outstanding regulatory aspects in the European pharmaceutical market. *Pharmacoeconomics* **15**, 519–533

Kanba, S. (1999) Disparities in drug development: the Japanese paradox. *Journal of Psychiatry and Neuroscience* **24**, 13–14

Kanehisa, M. (2000) *Post-genome informatics*, Oxford University Press, Oxford

Kettler, H.E. (1999) *Updating the cost of a new chemical entity*, Office of Health Economics, London

Kettler, H.E. and Casper, S. (2000) *The Road to sustainability in the UK and German biotechnology industries*, Office of Health Economics, London

Koenig, W. (2000) Heart disease and the inflammatory response. *British Medical Journal* 2000, 187–188

Kopelman, P.G. (2000) Obesity as a medical problem. *Nature* **404**, 635–643

Kotani, N., Oyama, T., Sakai, I. *et al.* (1997) Analgesic effect of a herbal medicine for treatment of primary dysmenorrhoea – a double-blind study. *American Journal of Chinese Medicine* **25**, 205–212

Kryzywicki, K. (2000) Parallel imports pose a threat to patient safety. *Pharmaceutical Times* **September**, 24–29

Lapierre, Y.D. (1998) Ethics and placebo. *Journal of Psychiatry and Neuroscience* **23**, 9–11

Lastra, R.M. (2000) The international monetary fund in historical perspective. *Journal of International Economic Law* **3**, 507–523

Laudan, I. (2000) Birth of the modern diet. *Scientific American* **August**, 62–67

Lee, K. and Mills, A. (2000) Strengthening governance for global health research. *British Medical Journal* **321**, 775–776

Lewis, D.B., Liggitt, H.D., Effmann, E.I. *et al.* (1993) Osteoporosis induced in mice by overproduction of interleukin 4. *Proceedings of the National Academy of Sciences of the USA* **90**, 11618–11622

Little, P. (1999) The book of genes. *Nature* **402**, 467–468

Ljungkvist, M.O., Andersson, D. and Gunnarsson, B. (1997) Cost and utilisation of pharmaceuticals in Sweden. *Health Policy* **41**(Suppl.), S55–S69

Lydiard, R.B. (1998) The role of drug therapy in social phobia. *Journal of Affective Disorders* **50**(Suppl. 1), S35–S9

Macarthur, D. (1995) The Japanese enigma. *Economics Medicines & Health* **Autumn**, 31–32

Mackay, F.J. (1998) Post-marketing studies: the work of the Drug Safety Research Unit. *Drug Safety* **19**, 343–353

Magnus, D. (1998) Disease gene patenting: the clinician's dilemma. *Cambridge Quarterly Healthcare Ethics* **7**, 433–435

Mann, C.C. and Plummer, M.L. (1991) *The aspirin wars*, Alfred A. Knopf, New York

*Marketletter* (2000) Chinese pharma 'soon to be a world force'. *Marketletter* **12 June**, 16

Maynard Smith, J. (1993) *The theory of evolution*. Canto, Cambridge

Miller, R. J. and Tran, P. B. (2000) More mysteries of opium reveal'd: 300 years of opiates. *TiPS* **21**, 299–304

Minghetti, P.M., Giudici, E.M. and Montanari, L. (2000a) A proposal to improve the supply of orphan drugs. *Pharmacological Research* **42**, 33–37

Minghetti, P., Casiraghi, A., Cilurzo, F. *et al.* (2000b) The situation of OTC drugs in Italy compared to the other EU states. *Pharmacological Research* **42**, 25–31

Mintzer, J. and Burns, A. (2000) Anticholinergic side-effects of drugs in elderly people. *Journal of the Royal Society of Medicine* **93**, 457–462

Mooney, G., Luckin, B. and Tanner, A. (1999) Patient pathways: solving the problem of institutional mortality in London during the later nineteenth century. *Social History of Medicine* **12**, 227–269

Mulgan, G. (1996) High tech and high angst. In: *The age of anxiety*, eds S. Dunant and R. Porter, Virago, London, pp. 1–20

*Nature* (2000) Benefits of increased public participation. *Nature* **405**, 259

Newbold, R.F. (1990) Patterns of anxiety in Sallust, Suetonius and Procopius. *Ancient History Bulletin* **4**, 44–50

Noyes, R. Jr, Moroz, G., Davidson, J.R. *et al.* (1997) Moclobemide in social phobia: a controlled dose-response trial. *Journal of Clinical Psychopharmacology* **17**, 247–254

Oakey, D. (2000) Drug money. *Investor's Chronicle* **14 July**, 24–27

Ono, S. and Kodama, Y. (2000) Clinical trials and the New Good Clinical Practice guideline in Japan. *Pharmacoeconomics* **18**, 125–141

Ottaway, P.B. (2000) Revised UK guidelines on medicinal products impact supplements and herbals. *Nutraceutical International* **May**, 7

Payer, L. (1989) *Medicine and culture*. Victor Gollancz, London

Peel, N. and Eastell, R. (1995) ABC of rheumatology: osteoporosis. *British Medical Journal* **310**, 989–992

*PharmaBusiness* (1999) Brand importance. *PharmaBusiness* **May**, 40–41

*Pharmaceutical Journal* (1999) Trends in procurement. *Pharmaceutical Journal* **263**, 832–833

Pilling, D. (2000) Patently overpriced: drug companies face Americans tired of high prices and poorer countries demanding cheaper life-saving drugs. *Financial Times* **30 July**

*Plough* (1933) Opening a pharmacy. *Plough* **21**, 9–11

Potzsch, R. (ed.) (1998) *The pharmacy: windows on history*. Editions Roche, Basel

Rawcliffe, C. (1995) *Medicine and society in later Medieval England*. Sutton Publishing, Stroud, Gloucestershire

Rawson, N.S., Pearce, G.L. and Inman, W.H. (1990) Prescription-event monitoring: methodology and recent progress. *Journal of Clinical Epidemiology* **43**, 509–522

Rey, R. (1993) *The history of pain*, Harvard University Press, Cambridge, MA

Richmond, M.H. (1999) *Human genomics: prospects for health care and public policy*, Pharmaceutical Partners, London

Rollin, B.E. (1995) *The Frankenstein syndrome: ethical and social issues in the genetic engineering of animals*, Cambridge University Press, Cambridge

Rose, G. (1993) *The strategy of preventive medicine*, Oxford Medical Publications, Oxford

Rose, P.G. and Lappas, P.T. (2000) Analysis of the cost effectiveness of concurrent cisplatin-based chemoradiation in cervical cancer: implications from five randomised trials. *Gynecologic Oncology* **78**, 3–6

Roughead, E.E., Harvey, K.J. and Gilbert, A.L. (1998) Commercial detailing techniques used by pharmaceutical sales representatives to influence prescribing. *Australian and New Zealand Journal of Medicine* **28**, 306–310

*Scientific American* (2000) Antihistamines and snake oil. *Scientific American* **May**, 10

*Scrip* (2000) Some drug prices higher in the developing world. *Scrip* **2553**,16

Sellars, J.A. (2000) The two faces of direct-to-consumer advertising *American Journal of Health-System Pharmacy* **57**, 1401

Senior, K.H.E. (2000) AIDS drug shows promise in clinical trials. *Molecular Medicine Today* **6**, 333–334

Shahi, G. and Cunningham. P. (1999) Facing change – turbulent times in Asia. *Pharmaceutical Industry Asia*, 3–5

Shapiro, M.F. (1997) Regulating pharmaceutical advertising: what will work? *Canadian Medical Association Journal* **156**, 359–361

Singer, P.A. (1993) *Practical ethics*, 2nd edn, Cambridge University Press, Cambridge

Singer, P.A. (2000) Medical ethics. *British Medical Journal* **321**, 282–285

Soni, S. (2000) Treatment of HIV infection – the road travelled and the journey ahead. *Inpharma* **16 September**, 3–4

Smith, L.D., Best, L.A., Stubbs, D.A. *et al.* (2000) Scientific graphs and the hierarchy of the sciences: A Latourian survey of inscription practices. *Social Studies of Science* **30**, 73–94

Sneader, W. (1998) The discovery of heroin. *Lancet* **352**, 1697–1699

Takahashi, H., Pool, V., Tsail, T.F. *et al.* (2000) Adverse events after Japanese encephalitis vaccination: review of post-marketing surveillance data from Japan and the US. *Vaccine* **18**, 2963–2969

Takehara, J. and Yamada, H. (1999) The development of the Japanese pharmaceutical industry (part 7). Histories of medical advertisements from Taisho Era till Showa Era. *Yakushigaku Zasshi* **34**, 77–82.

Tan, Y.-T., Tillett, D.J. and McKay, I.A. (2000) Molecular strategies for overcoming antibiotic resistance in bacteria. *Molecular Medicine Today* **6**, 309–314

Taylor, A. (2000) *Is civil society heard in Brussels?* Federal Trust, London

Timmermans, S. and Leiter, V. (2000) The redemption of thalidomide: standardising the risk of birth defects. *Social Studies of Science* **30**, 41–71

Trial, R. (2000) The drug industry to take AIDS drugs to Africa. *Pharmaceutical Business News* **24 May**, 5

Tribble, J.L. (1998) Gene patents – a pharmaceutical perspective. *Cambridge Quarterly of Healthcare Ethics* **7**, 429–432

Valler, M.J. and Green, D. (2000) Diversity screening versus focussed screening in drug discovery. *Drug Discovery Today* **5**, 286–293

Vray, M. and Attali, J.R. (1995) Randomised study of glibenclamide versus traditional Chinese treatment in type 2 diabetic patients. Chinese–French Scientific Committee for the Study of Diabetes. *Diabetes and Metabolism* **21**, 433–439

Walsh, G. (1998) *Biopharmaceuticals: biochemistry and biotechnology*, John Wiley, Chichester

Wang, T.J., Ausiello, J.C. and Stafford, R.S. (1999) Trends in antihypertensive drug advertising, 1985–1996. *Circulation* **99**, 2055–2057

Willis, J. (2000) Pharma on trial: making medicines for children safer. *Scrip* **September**, 11–13

Wong, I.C.K. and Sweis, D. (2000) Techniques in pharmacovigilance *Pharmaceutical Journal* **264**, 922–923

Xu, X.J., Banerjee, P., Rustin, M.H. *et al.* (1997) Modulation by Chinese herbal therapy of immune mechanisms in the skin of patients with atopic eczema. *British Journal of Dermatology* **136**, 54–59

Yamakawa, K. (1995a) Historical sketch of modern pharmaceutical science and technology (part 3). From the second half of the 19th century to World War II. *Yakushigaku Zasshi* **30**, 1–10.

Yamakawa, K. (1995b) Historical sketch of modern pharmaceutical science and technology (part 4). Post World War II – 50 years. *Yakushigaku Zasshi* **30**, 75–90

Young, S.N. (1998) Risk in research – from the Nuremberg Code to the Tri-Council Code: implications for clinical trials of psychotropic drugs. *Journal of Psychiatry and Neuroscience* **23**, 149–155

Young, S.N. and Palmour, R.M. (1999) Research on genes: promises and limitations. *Journal of Psychiatry and Neuroscience* **24**, 300–303.

Zanfei, A. (2000) Transnational firms and the changing organisation of innovative activities *Cambridge Journal of Economics* **24**, 515–542

# Internet resources

Abbott Laboratories: http://www.abbott.com/

American Home Products: http://www.ahp.com/

Amgen: http://www.amgen.com/

AstraZeneca: http://www.astrazeneca.com/

Aventis: http://www.aventis.com/

Bayer: http://www.bayer.com/

Boehringer Ingelheim: http://www.boehringer-ingelheim.com/corporate

Bristol-Myers Squibb: http://www.bms.com/landing.html

*British Medical Journal*: http://www.bmj.com

Dow Jones: http://dowjones.wsj.com/DJReg.jsp

Eli Lilly: http://www.lilly.com/

European Gene Vector Database and Sales Repository: http://www.egdr.org

European Medicine Evaluation Agency: http://www.eudra.org/emea.html

Evista.com: http://www.evista.com/

Food and Drug Administration: http://www.fda.gov/

Fosamax.com: http://www.fosamax.com

Foundation for Osteoporosis Research and Education: http://www.fore.org/)

FTSE: http://www.ftse.com/

Glaxo Wellcome: http://www.glaxowellcome.co.uk/;
http://www.glaxowellcome.com/

International Conference of Harmonisation: http://www.ifpma.org/ich1.html

International Federation of Pharmaceutical Manufacturers Associations:
http://www.ifpma.org/

International Monetary Fund: http://www.imf.org/

International Osteoporosis Foundation: http://www.osteofound.org/).

Johnson & Johnson: http://www.jnj.com/

Medicines Control Agency: http://www.open.gov.uk/mca/mcahome.htm

Medline: http://igm.nlm.nih.gov/

Merck & Co: http://www.merck.com/

Monsanto: http://www.monsanto.com/

Nasdaq: http://www.nasdaq.com/

National Osteoporosis Foundation: http://www.nof.org/

National Osteoporosis Society: http://www.nos.org.uk

Novartis: http://www.novartis.com/

Online Ethics for Engineering and Science: http://www.onlineethics.org

Organisation for Economic Co-operation and Development:
http://www.oecd.org/

Pfizer: http://www.pfizer.com/main.html

Pharmaceutical Research and Manufacturers of America: http://www.phrma.org/

Pharmacia & Upjohn: http://www.pnu.com/
Proctor & Gamble: http://www.pg.com/
Prozac: http://www.prozac.com
Roche: http://www.roche.com/
Sanofi-Synthélabo: http://www.sanofi-synthelabo.com/fr/index.asp
Schering AG: http://www.schering.de/eng
Schering-Plough: http://www.sgp.com/
SmithKline Beecham: http://www.sb.com/
Takeda Chemical Co.: http://www.takeda.com/ and
http://www.takeda.com/index-e.html
TAP: http://www.tap.com/
World Bank: http://www.worldbank.org/
World Health Organization: http://www.who.dk/
World Intellectual Property Organization: http://www.wipo.org/
World Trade Organization: http://www.wto.org/
Yahoo: http://www.yahoo.com